Understanding New Labour's Market Reforms of the English NHS

Edited by Nicholas Mays, Anna Dixon and Lorelei Jones

The Kings Fund›

The King's Fund seeks to understand how the health system in England can be improved. Using that insight, we help to shape policy, transform services and bring about behaviour change. Our work includes research, analysis, leadership development and service improvement. We also offer a wide range of resources to help everyone working in health to share knowledge, learning and ideas.

Published by
The King's Fund
11-13 Cavendish Square
London W1G 0AN
Tel: 020 7307 2591
Fax: 020 7307 2801
www.kingsfund.org.uk

First published 2011 by The King's Fund

Charity registration number: 1126980

ISBN: 978 1 85717 626 1

A catalogue record for this publication is available from the British Library

Available from:
The King's Fund
11-13 Cavendish Square
London W1G 0AN
Tel: 020 7307 2591
Fax: 020 7307 2801
Email: publications@kingsfund.org.uk
www.kingsfund.org.uk/publications

Edited by Fiona Weston

Typeset by Grasshopper Design Company

Printed and bound in the UK by the MPG Books Group, Bodmin and King's Lynn

Contents

List of figures and tables

List of abbreviations

AHC	annual health check
CHI	Commission for Health Improvement
CQC	Care Quality Commission
CQUIN	Commissioning for Quality and Innovation
CGR	clinical governance reviews
DHA	district health authority
DRG	diagnosis-related group
GP	general practitioner
HHI	Herfindahl-Hirschman index
HMO	health maintenance organisation
HRG	healthcare resource group
ISTC	independent-sector treatment centre
IVF	*in vitro* fertilisation
LGA	Local Government Association
MIU	minor injury unit
NICE	National Institute for Health and Clinical Excellence
NHS	National Health Service
NSF	National Service Framework
OPM	Office for Public Management
PBC	practice-based commissioning
PbR	Payment by Results
PCT	primary care trust
PSA	public service agreement
SHAs	strategic health authority
TSO	third-sector organisation
WCC	World Class Commissioning

About the authors

Pauline Allen is Senior Lecturer in Service Delivery and Organisational Research at the London School of Hygiene and Tropical Medicine. She is also qualified as a solicitor, and practised company commercial law for some years before changing careers to research. She uses socio-legal theory, institutional economics and organisational theory to study the governance of organisations in the NHS and the relationships between them. Her current research interests include NHS foundation trusts, contracting in the NHS, accountability and regulation, social enterprises and the increasing diversity of types of providers to NHS patients.

Gwyn Bevan is Professor of Management Science in the Department of Management at the London School of Economics and Political Science. He has worked as an academic at Warwick Business School and in medical schools in London and Bristol. He has also worked in industry, consulting, the Treasury, and for the Commission for Health Improvement (CHI). His current research includes studies of outcomes of the natural experiment of different policies in UK countries for the NHS and schools following devolution; and the SyMPOSE (Systems Modelling for Performance Optimisation and Service Equity) project funded by the Health Foundation, which is a programme of collaborative research that aims to reduce expenditure on health care with least harm to the health of populations and without widening inequalities in health.

Seán Boyle is Senior Research Fellow at LSE Health and Social Care at the London School of Economics and Political Science. He writes on a range of health policy issues and recently published the *Health Systems in Transition* report on England, a comprehensive overview of the health and social care system in England. Drawing on detailed analysis of changes to health care introduced by Labour governments between 1997 and 2010 the report assesses their impact in terms of access, equity, efficiency, quality and health outcomes. Seán is also a health planning and policy consultant with considerable experience of working at senior level in both the public and private sector, and has a detailed knowledge of the public policy environment.

Natasha Curry is a Senior Fellow at The Nuffield Trust, prior to which she spent six years at The King's Fund. Her research interests include commissioning, long-term conditions management and integrated care. She led The King's Fund evaluation of practice-based commissioning and managed the work programme on predicting the risk of emergency admissions. Natasha previously worked as a consultant at Matrix, a research and consultancy company, prior to which she was evaluation officer at the Chinese National Healthy Living Centre.

Anna Dixon is Director of Policy at The King's Fund. She has conducted research and published widely on health care funding and policy in the United Kingdom and Europe. She was previously a lecturer in European Health Policy at the London School of Economics and was awarded the Commonwealth Fund Harkness Fellowship in Health Care Policy in 2005–6. She has also worked in the Strategy Unit at the Department of Health and is a visiting Fellow at LSE Health.

Jennifer Dixon has researched and written widely on health care reform in the United Kingdom and internationally. She trained originally in medicine, practising mainly paediatric medicine, before a career in policy analysis. She has a Masters in public health and a PhD in health services research from the London School of Hygiene and Tropical Medicine. Until January 2008 she was director of policy at The King's Fund, London. She was a Harkness Fellow in New York in 1990, studying the obstacles to comprehensive health reform in the United States, and was the policy adviser to the Chief Executive of the National Health Service between 1998 and 2000. She is currently a board member of the Audit Commission, and until recently was on the Board of the Healthcare Commission. She is visiting professor at LSE, Imperial College and London School of Hygiene and Tropical Medicine.

Shelley Farrar is a Research Fellow and leader for the Performance and Organisation research theme within the Behaviour, Health and Health Systems programme of the Health Economics Research Unit at the University of Aberdeen. Shelley graduated from the University of Strathclyde with a BA in Economics in 1989 and joined the Health Economics Research Unit after working at the Scottish Office as an Economic Assistant. She has since gained an MSc in Economics from Glasgow University and a PhD in Economics from the University of Aberdeen. Her research interests primarily lie with organisational performance and the evaluation of policy methods to improve performance. She is also interested in the motivation of decision-makers in the NHS and how that might affect their responses to incentives.

Lorelei Jones is a Research Fellow at the London School of Hygiene and Tropical Medicine. She holds a BA (Hons) in Anthropology and an MSc in health services/systems research from the LSHTM. Before joining the School in 2007, she held research posts at the Royal College of Obstetricians and Gynaecologists, the British Medical Association and the Department of Nursing at the University of Technology, Sydney. Her research interests are in UK health policy and health services, especially the anthropology of policy and the sociology of health service organisation and she is currently working towards a PhD looking at policy discourse and the planning of hospital services in the English NHS.

Nicholas Mays is Professor of Health Policy in the Department of Health Services Research and Policy at the London School of Hygiene and Tropical Medicine where he has been since 2003. He is scientific co-ordinator of the Department of Health-funded Health Reforms Evaluation Programme, which aims to evaluate the impact of two sets of major reforms of the English NHS: first, the market-related reforms of the period 2002–10; and second, the changes following the 2008 Next Stage Review, *High Quality Care for All*. Since January 2011, he has also directed the Department of Health-funded Policy Innovation Research Unit, a new venture aimed at involving a multidisciplinary team of researchers in the very earliest stages of national policy development across health services, social care and public health. From 1994 to 1998 he was Director of Health Services Research at The King's Fund, London.

Carol Propper is Professor of Economics and Head of the Healthcare Management Group at Imperial College Business School. She also holds an appointment at the University of Bristol, where she helped found the Centre for Market and Public Organisation, which has attracted major research funding from a number of bodies. Carol was Senior Economic Advisor to NHS Executive on regulation of the NHS internal market 1993–4, Co-Director of the Centre for the Analysis of Social Exclusion at London School of Economics from 1997 to 2007, Co-Director and Director of the Centre for Market and Public Organisation from 1998 to 2009, and chaired the ESRC research grants board until 2009. She is particularly interested in the impact of incentives on the quality of health care delivery and, more widely, on the design and consequences of incentives within the public sector and the boundary between the state and private markets. Carol has been awarded a CBE for her services to social science. The accolade recognises Carol's research into public economics and economics of health care as well as her work with colleagues from other social science and medical disciplines.

Ruth Robertson is a senior research associate for the Affordable Health Insurance Program at The Commonwealth Fund in New York, a private foundation that aims to promote a high-performing health system. Ms Robertson tracks, researches, and writes about emerging policy issues related to US health reform, the comprehensiveness and affordability of health insurance coverage, and access to care. She previously worked for The King's Fund in London, as a senior health policy researcher, where her work focused on various aspects of health system reform in the English National Health Service. Ms Robertson holds a BA in Economics from the University of Nottingham and an MSc in Social Policy and Planning from the London School of Economics and Political Science.

Judith Smith is an experienced and widely published health services researcher and policy analyst at The Nuffield Trust. Before joining The Nuffield Trust she was Senior Lecturer and Director of Research at the Health Services Management Centre, University of Birmingham. From 2007 to 2009 she was Visiting Senior Research

Fellow at the Health Services Research Centre, Victoria University of Wellington, New Zealand, and adviser on primary health care reform to the New Zealand Ministry of Health. Her research is focused on health commissioning, physician organisations, health management and leadership, and primary care. Judith's other roles include being a member of the board of the UK health services research network and acting as expert adviser on health organisation and commissioning to the Mid Staffordshire NHS Foundation Trust Public Inquiry.

Deokhee Yi is a Research Fellow in the Health Economics Research Unit at the University of Aberdeen. She holds a BSc degree in Pharmacy and Master of Public Health (Economics major) from the Seoul National University and a PhD in Health Economics from the University of North Carolina at Chapel Hill. Since joining HERU in 2005, she has been working on policy evaluations with large data sets, preference elicitations in primary care and lifestyle intervention programmes using discrete choice experiments and economic modelling for lifestyle intervention programmes. Her research interests also include labour market and health, inequality in health and health econometrics.

Acknowledgements

This book is very much the product of a team effort. We are very grateful to the individual chapter authors for the time and care that they put into their initial drafts and in subsequently responding to our comments and editorial suggestions. The bulk of the early work in securing the authors' contributions and pulling the book into shape fell to Lorelei, but towards the end of the process, Stefanie Tan very ably assisted Nicholas Mays and Anna Dixon in Lorelei Jones's absence on maternity leave. We are very grateful to Stefanie Tan for her persistence and attention to detail, chasing down missing references and cross-checking for consistency – no mean feat with many authors and a tight deadline.

Thanks are also due to Julian Le Grand for reviewing all the chapters and for writing the foreword, and to Chris Ham for helpful comments on the manuscript.

At or near the core of most of the chapters are summaries of the findings of the studies in the first wave of the Health Reform Evaluation Programme, which was commissioned and funded by the Department of Health's Policy Research Programme and co-ordinated by one of the editors (Mays).

However, this book is an independent report. The views expressed in it are not necessarily those of the Department of Health.

Nicholas Mays
Anna Dixon
Lorelei Jones
London, July 2011

Foreword

Julian Le Grand

I came to this book with some trepidation. Both informally as a university academic, and later more formally as an adviser to the prime minister, I was deeply involved in the genesis, development and implementation of the National Health Service (NHS) reforms that the researchers set out to evaluate.

Although I believed that the theoretical basis of the reforms was sufficiently strong for them to work in practice, I could not know that they would. Reading this book would tell me if my faith in my theories was well founded or – as is so often the case when theoretical analyses encounter the complexity of the real world – naïve at best and disastrous at worst.

Indeed, at the time the reforms were being implemented, there were plenty of people prepared to predict disaster. Proposals for change within an institution as revered as the NHS always provoke extreme reactions – as the current coalition government has discovered. Accusations abounded: of privatisation, of handing over the NHS to the hands of evil US corporations, of pandering to middle-class obsessions with choice, of exacerbating health and health care inequalities, of creating chaos and fragmentation, and of fatally undermining the public realm. Alleged virtue was suddenly discovered in the old ways of doing things, such as central planning, professional networks and institutional collaboration, although in practice these existed only rarely and, where they did exist, worked even more rarely. Nonetheless, they all acquired the glow of a lost golden age when the NHS was effective, efficient and equitable; where there was no waste, where no one waited months or years for treatments for simple conditions such as hernias or cataracts, where no one languished for 24 hours on a trolley in the accident and emergency department, and where the middle classes were not privileged in their access to specialist care. Of course, no such NHS had ever existed, but that did not stop the tsunami of criticism that threatened the very existence of the reforms before they had begun.

However, it would seem that both my worries and those of the critics were misplaced. It is hard to resist the impression from this book that, on balance, the reforms have worked. The dire predictions of apocalypse have not materialised. In 2010, the English NHS was delivering a higher quality, more efficient and even more equitable service than it had when implementation of the reforms began in 2003. Some of the improvement was undoubtedly due to the legacy of the policy referred to here as 'targets and terror', and some is the result of increased resources, although comparisons with the better resourced but worse performing unreformed NHS in Scotland and Wales suggest that resources might not be as important as initially thought. But the researchers have also demonstrated that patient choice and provider competition have had independent effects and, more importantly, positive ones in exactly the direction that the theory predicted. As yet, some of the improvements are modest, but they seem to be gathering momentum as the reforms bed down.

There are lessons here both for governments engaging in health service reform and for their critics. Policy-makers need to have well-designed policies that have a good basis in theory and, where available, in evidence, and that address what are generally agreed to be the real problems with the system (failure to do so is a mistake dogging the current coalition government's reform process). Critics need to beware of listening too hard to those with vested interests in the status quo, and of rushing to premature judgements of apocalypse and disaster that subsequently look foolish. In order to learn those lessons fully, all of those involved in the reform process should read this book.

Julian Le Grand
London, July 2011

1 Return to the market: objectives and evolution of New Labour's market reforms

Nicholas Mays, Anna Dixon and Lorelei Jones

Market-like mechanisms began to be introduced into the National Health Service (NHS) in England from 2002. Aimed at improving system performance, these interrelated policy changes comprised:

- giving patients a choice of provider

- stronger commissioning (including practice-based commissioning)

- greater provider diversity

- increased autonomy for publicly owned hospitals

- activity-based payments for acute providers (so-called Payment by Results)

- revisions of the regulatory framework.

This package of policies was intended to create a system that was patient-centred and 'self-improving' (Department of Health 2005a) (*see* Figure 1 overleaf). The key objectives were better care, better patient experience and better value for money.

Although similar in some respects to the internal market reforms introduced between 1991 and 1997 by the then Conservative government, these changes went further towards creating a market (rather than simply an internal market). For example, because individual patients were now being offered a choice of hospital for elective care, it was their decisions, rather than those of a third-party commissioning organisation, that became the drivers of the allocation of some of the resources.

The aim of this book is to review the evidence on the implementation and impact of the market-related reforms in the English NHS under New Labour. This is important for two reasons:

- New Labour's changes represented a major attempt to improve an iconic public service using market-related incentives

- the coalition government is currently pursuing a very similar logic in its own proposed reforms.

Figure 1 The framework for NHS market reforms begun in 2002

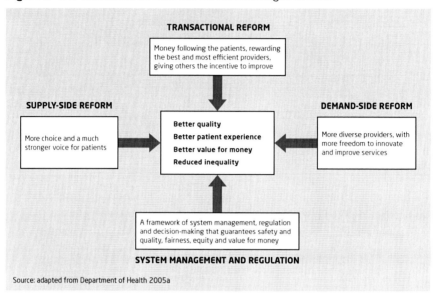

Source: adapted from Department of Health 2005a

The experience of the latter part of the 2000s should therefore provide valuable insights into the challenges and potential benefits that the coalition's changes are likely to bring.

At the core of the review of the evidence are the studies of different aspects of New Labour's reforms that were funded by the Department of Health through the Health Reform Evaluation Programme and undertaken between 2006 and 2010. One of this book's editors (Mays) was the scientific co-ordinator of this programme.

The remainder of this chapter introduces the market reforms and considers how they differed from the internal market of 1991–7. It also discusses the rationale underlying the reforms, and the concerns raised by commentators when they were introduced. It concludes with an overview of the structure of the book, and the approach taken in each chapter to evaluate the market reforms.

The internal market 1991–7

The idea of introducing market-like incentives into the NHS was first posited by Alain Enthoven (1985). It was intended to motivate improvements in efficiency and patient responsiveness while maintaining a tax-financed system that provided universal free access to health services. In 1989, the Conservative government led by Margaret Thatcher published the White Paper *Working for Patients* (Department of Health 1989), which outlined the introduction of an internal market in the NHS. This became law as the NHS and Community Care Act 1990, and the internal market was implemented with effect from April 1991.

It was structured around a novel separation of the roles of purchaser and provider within the NHS. District health authorities (DHAs) became the main purchasers. They were financed according to the needs of their resident populations, and were free to buy hospital and community health services from any provider, whether in the public, private or voluntary sector (although the vast majority of NHS services continued to be provided by the public sector).

Acute hospitals and other NHS providers (eg, of mental health services) became 'trusts', statutory corporations free from DHA control. Trusts were funded on their ability to win contracts to undertake an agreed amount of work for a DHA at a locally negotiated price. The theoretical incentive for providers was, therefore, to minimise costs and maximise quality in order to stay in business.

At the same time, general practitioner (GP) practices could opt to become 'fundholders', allowing them to hold their own budgets for the non-emergency hospital outpatient and elective surgical, diagnostic and pharmaceutical care of the patients on their lists. They were expected to act as informed agents on behalf of their patients, securing timely access to care from providers, and to negotiate their own secondary care contracts, decide which providers, services and patients would benefit from their funds, and keep any surpluses generated (Kay 2002).

Despite being widely heralded as the most radical change in the NHS since its inception (Butler 1992); the NHS internal market did not produce the degree of measurable change predicted by proponents and feared by opponents (Mays *et al* 2000). In terms of efficiency, there is some evidence that the costs of providing hospital services fell faster than in the previous decade (Mulligan 1998) and that productivity (the ratio of outputs to inputs) rose (Söderlund *et al* 1997), although management and administrative costs increased, driven by the need to negotiate and monitor contracts between purchasers and providers (Paton 1995).

In terms of equity, there was little evidence of the discrimination against chronically ill or high-cost patients that critics of the internal market had feared. However, there is little doubt (though also little good research) that a 'two-tier' system did operate. GP fundholders used their budgets to extend the services available within their own premises and, on average, secured shorter hospital waiting times for their patients than did health authorities (Dusheiko *et al* 2004). Nevertheless, the waiting time for inpatient treatment (especially those longer than 18 months) fell for all NHS patients during the 1990s.

There is little evidence on the impact of the internal market on the quality of care. Propper *et al* (2004, 2008a) showed that hospitals in the 1990s operating in areas with higher levels of competition appeared to produce poorer patient outcomes, at least as measured by indicators such as death rates after surgery for heart disease. They concluded that price competition had not resulted in quality improvements.

The principal explanation for the limited impact of the internal market lies in the way it was implemented. As one systematic evaluation concluded: 'the incentives were too weak and the constraints too strong' (Le Grand *et al* 1998, p 130). Central government limited the impact of competition between providers, particularly because allowing inefficient providers to fail or close might have threatened other goals such as equity of access, or caused political embarrassment. The exception was GP fundholders, who were given the freedom to change the pattern of referrals and shift resources accordingly, in part because they accounted for a relatively small proportion of the workload of any single hospital. During this period, the NHS was driven at least as much by central directives (eg, on reducing waiting times) as by the internal market.

Another limitation of the internal market concerned the provision of information, what Enthoven (2000) calls 'the oxygen of markets' (p 106). This significantly curtailed the potential of the internal market to produce improvements in quality. As Enthoven notes: 'Data on pediatric heart surgery mortality at the Bristol Royal Infirmary, for example, apparently were not available to the local health authority, which meant that the authority could not stop buying services from a provider with an unacceptably high mortality rate' (p 108).

Whatever the internal market might have failed to achieve, it is clear that it brought fundamental changes to the culture and operation of the NHS. Providers had to be far more aware than in the past of the quality and cost of what they provided. Purchasers came to question traditional ways of providing services and encouraged providers to think of new models of care that were more relevant to the needs of patients, such as the development of specialist outreach services in the community, early discharge schemes, shared and intermediate forms of care between hospitals and general practices, the use of skilled nurse practitioners rather than medical staff, and so on. GP fundholding significantly increased the ability of GPs to influence the way in which hospital specialists provided care to their patients. It also increased the degree of communication between primary and secondary care (Glennerster *et al* 1994; Smith *et al* 2004; Smith *et al* 2005).

Labour's approach to the market: the early years

In May 1997, New Labour came to power. Under its leadership, NHS reforms continued, but with a new focus on collaboration rather than the competition-based system that the preceding Conservative government had championed.

The new government began by claiming to abolish the internal market, which it regarded as an administratively wasteful failure. However, one core feature remained intact – the separation of purchasers and providers – although the term 'purchasing' was removed from the NHS lexicon to be replaced by 'commissioning', in order to reflect a shift away from simply buying from the existing range of services offered by providers, towards developing new and better services by working with providers to improve their ability to meet the needs of the local population.

GP fundholding was abolished on the grounds that it had led to a 'two-tier' service, and primary care groups involving all GPs were established. These groups had indicative budgets, and were intended gradually to take over the responsiblility for commissioning from the health authorities. They eventually became statutory bodies with their own budgets in the shape of primary care trusts (PCTs), and replaced health authorities as the principal commissioners of NHS services at local level.

In this way, New Labour appeared to share the Conservatives' support for the concept of giving primary care providers responsibility for purchasing and organising most of the health care needed by their patients. However, during the first term of the New Labour government, particularly when Frank Dobson was Secretary of State for Health, the focus of health policy was on securing national standards of quality, and against provider competition of any kind. Between 1999 and 2002, two new regulatory and oversight organisations were established – the Commission for Health Improvement (CHI) (which later became the Healthcare Commission and is now the Care Quality Commission(CQC)) and the National Institute for Clinical Excellence (which later joined with the Health Development Agency to become the National Institute for Health and Clinical Excellence) – and the first national service frameworks (NSFs) were introduced. The last were evidence- and professional consensus-based articulations of what a 'good' service for a particular condition or patient group should look like, and were influential with both commissioners and providers.

During this time, the thrust of reforms was marked by a strong focus on top-down policy-making that saw the setting of national standards (through NSFs) and targets (eg, for reducing waiting times) as a means of standardising care across providers (Stevens 2004).

The period was also one in which the government stuck with the tight spending plans for the NHS that it had inherited from the Conservatives. It was not until 2000, following Tony Blair's announcement that per capita spending on the NHS would rise to match the EU average, that there was significant growth in the NHS budget.

The Labour government decided to pursue a policy of 'investment and reform' in the English NHS (with effect from 1999 the responsibility for NHS policy in Wales and Scotland had passed to the Welsh Assembly and Scottish Parliament, respectively) to ensure that the increased spending delivered the desired results, particularly on the 1997 election promise to shorten waiting times. By 2002, a consensus appears to have formed among ministers and their advisers that the existing 'command and control' policies, such as the setting and enforcement of targets, had reached their limit of likely impact and needed to be augmented by other policy instruments. There were fears that the increased resources would be dissipated and would not generate a commensurate improvement in performance without further support. The conclusion was reached that a return to a greater emphasis on supplier competition was required to make the most efficient use of resources and meet patient and public expectations (Stevens 2004). Thus the market reforms can be seen as an attempt to 'sharpen' the incentives in the system to ensure that large increases in funding would deliver tangible improvements in performance.

Labour's market reforms

Labour's reintroduction of explicit market-like mechanisms was a gradual, pragmatic process rather than a one-off overarching 'big bang' set of reforms (*see* Figure 2 below). On the commissioning side of the NHS market, PCTs were established in 2002 (Walshe *et al* 2004) and given the responsibility for commissioning NHS services on behalf of a defined geographical population. Their budgets were allocated in relation to the relative needs of their populations.

Figure 2 Policy timeline

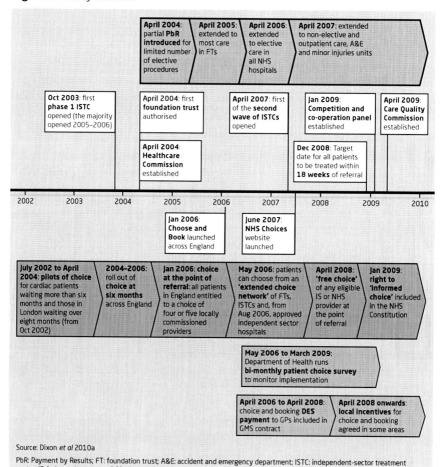

Source: Dixon *et al* 2010a

PbR: Payment by Results; FT: foundation trust; A&E: accident and emergency department; ISTC: independent-sector treatment centre; IS: independent sector; DES: directed enhanced service; GP: general practitioners; GMS: general medical services

From 2004, PCTs were required to devolve part of their budgets to general practices (under a scheme called practice-based commissioning). This once again allowed GPs to shape the pattern of local services directly, although the budgets they were given were indicative and the PCT remained responsible for the contracts and spending of the practice-based commissioners.

Following a reorganisation in 2006, the number of PCTs was reduced from 303 to 152, many of which were co-terminous with local authorities.

From as early as 1999, the Department of Health had introduced NHS diagnostic and treatment centres – stand-alone centres on NHS hospital sites specialising in routine diagnostics and high volumes of low-risk, straightforward operations that did not require hospital admission – in order to accelerate the reduction of waiting lists and times. This programme was extended in 2002 to include nationally commissioned surgical treatment centres provided by the private sector. While the independent-sector treatment centres (ISTCs) were a further contribution to the task of expanding and speeding up elective surgery by increasing the capacity available to the NHS, it was also significant that they represented an alternative to NHS providers, signalling the government's growing willingness to allow greater competition in the treatment of NHS patients in the future.

The NHS Plan (Department of Health 2000b) stated that patients would be able to choose the times and dates of their hospital appointments, but this was initially about increasing convenience for patients, not about driving competition. From 2002, with the publication of *Delivering the NHS Plan: Next steps on investment, next steps on reform*, patients were offered the choice of being treated by an alternative provider if they could not be treated within six months by the NHS, as a way of reducing waiting times and making better use of existing capacity (Department of Health 2002a). In *The NHS Improvement Plan: Putting people at the heart of public services*, published in 2004, the aim of offering patients a choice of provider so as to reduce waiting times was broadened to encompass improving patient responsiveness, increasing efficiency and improving quality (Department of Health 2004d). From January 2006, NHS patients were to be offered a choice of five providers at the point of referral, of which at least one had to be from the independent sector. In January 2008, this was extended yet further to the choice of any accredited provider (so-called 'free choice').

In order that money could follow the patients and provide an incentive for efficient providers to increase throughput, the NHS introduced an activity-based payment system for hospitals known as Payment by Results (PbR). The system of fixed national prices was based on health resource groups – the UK adaptation of the US system of diagnosis-related groups. The fixed price for each health resource group was calculated on the basis of average costs.

PbR was gradually introduced from 2003/4, initially in higher-performing NHS trusts known as foundation trusts (*see* below), with the intention of moving, in due course, to a system in which all NHS activity would be paid for using a standard tariff. It was introduced first for elective care, followed by emergency care, and attendance at and procedures in accident and emergency departments (A&E) and outpatient clinics. By 2006/7, the tariff had been extended across all NHS providers to cover admitted patient care, and outpatient and A&E attendances. However, even within the acute hospital sector, many activities continued to remain outside PbR, including critical care, mental health care, community health services, ambulance services and primary care. In 2009/10, only £26 billion of English NHS activity, out of a total of £105 billion, was paid for under PbR (House of Commons Health Committee 2010b).

From 2003, high-performing NHS trusts were given the opportunity to apply to become free-standing, non-profitmaking, public benefit corporations known as NHS foundation trusts. These remained part of the NHS, but were given greater financial and managerial freedoms (eg, they could borrow from the private sector up to limits set by the regulator, and develop joint ventures with the private sector). Unlike ordinary NHS trusts, the Secretary of State for Health cannot direct foundation trusts. Instead, an independent economic regulator known as Monitor, established in 2004, authorises them and oversees their compliance with authorisation. It was intended that all NHS trusts should achieve foundation status by 2014.

New Labour had already established a quality regulator for NHS trust care before embarking on the gradual reintroduction of market forces. The Commission for Health Improvement had been established in 2000 to oversee the quality of local services and remedy shortcomings. It was replaced in 2004 by the Healthcare Commission, which was responsible for monitoring the performance of NHS providers against a set of quality and safety measures, as well as for ensuring that independent providers met minimum safety and quality standards. In 2009, it was superseded by the Care Quality Commission. Created from an amalgamation of the existing inspectorates responsible for health care, mental health and social care, the Care Quality Commission is responsible for the inspection and quality regulation of all health and social care providers, both public and private, in England.

It is apparent from this very brief narrative that the (re-)emergence of the market under New Labour occurred gradually. It was only fully articulated as a coherent set of reforms in 2005 (*see* Figure 1, p 2). *Health Reform in England: Update and next steps* (Department of Health 2005a) presented the different elements of the emerging market as a package of interrelated reforms designed to 'embed within the healthcare system incentives for continuous improvement (p 15)'. The ambitious aims of these reforms can be summarised as: improving quality of care, improving patient experience, improving value for money, and reducing inequality. The main elements of the reform package are summarised in Table 1, opposite, and are the focus of this book.

Table 1 Components of New Labour's NHS market reforms by 2005

Supply-side	■ The development of more diverse providers of clinical services, including independent-sector treatment centres ■ Greater independence and autonomy for publicly owned providers as foundation trusts
Demand-side	■ Primary care trusts responsible for commissioning the majority of NHS services ■ General practices delegated budgets for specific services, called practice-based commissioning ■ Patients given a choice of provider at the point of referral to secondary care
Transactional	■ Activity-based payment for hospitals called Payment by Results, comprising a fixed price based on average costs
System management and regulation	■ Foundation trusts subject to authorisation by the independent regulator Monitor ■ The performance of primary care trusts assessed by the Care Quality Commission and strategic health authorities ■ Minimum safety and quality standards enforced by the Care Quality Commission

Comparing the internal market of the 1990s with New Labour's market

Table 2, below, summarises the differences between the market introduced by the Conservatives in 1991 and the market reforms instigated by New Labour. Although

Table 2 Differences between the 1991 and 2002 market reforms

NHS market, 1991-97	NHS market, 2002-10
■ Patient choice restricted to fundholding GPs	■ Patient choice of elective provider
Health authority purchasing ■ Contracts not subject to contract law	**Primary care trust commissioning** ■ Contracts legally binding
Fundholding ■ Voluntary ■ Fundholders able to retain surpluses	**Practice-based commissioning** ■ Universal, at least for primary care trusts ■ Intention that any surpluses be shared with primary care trust
NHS trusts ■ Some price competition ■ Unable to retain surpluses ■ In practice, access to new sources of capital restricted and not free to borrow commercially	**Foundation trusts** ■ Paid increasingly using fixed prices under Payment by Results ■ Surpluses can be retained to reinvest ■ Commercial borrowing possible within limits
Evaluation ■ No independent evaluation studies until late in the reform process	**Evaluation** ■ Programme of independent evaluation studies commissioned by Department of Health

the legislation to create the original NHS trusts was similar in many regards to the legislation to create foundation trusts, the latter went further, breaking the link of accountability to the Secretary of State and creating new local governance arrangements. In the internal market, independent regulation and systems of performance management were underdeveloped. The establishment and growth in the number of independent regulators of public services is a marked feature of the Labour government's period in office (Thorlby and Maybin 2010). Under the Conservatives, general practice fundholding was explicitly voluntary, whereas all practices were nominally participants in PCTs and were represented in the professional executive committee of the PCT, because the Labour government wished to bring the advantages of the previous GP fundholding scheme to all registered patients. On the other hand, like fundholding, the later practice-based commissioning scheme was also voluntary to some degree, at least for practices, if not for the PCTs. The government required all PCTs to implement it, but some did so more enthusiastically than others (Curry *et al* 2008).

For all the policy rhetoric about giving patients more choice, the reality for non-fundholding GPs in the 1990s internal market was that their referrals were limited to those hospitals with which their health authority had contracts. Thus for many GPs it seemed as if there were less, not more, choice. Under Labour, patient choice was supported by incentives for GPs and a new electronic referral and booking system called Choose and Book. There was also investment in information support to help patients to choose providers on the basis of indicators of the quality of their care.

Unlike the 1990s internal market, in which prices were negotiated locally, within the New Labour market there was no price competition, at least for the services included in the PbR scheme. By giving patients a choice of provider, and introducing competition under fixed prices, the Labour government sought to strengthen the incentives for efficiency, responsiveness and quality, and address some of the constraints on the impact of the 1990s internal market.

Critique of the market reforms

The market reforms were based on the view that competition among providers creates incentives for them to improve the efficiency and quality of their services to meet the demands of purchasers, and that this process can be made to occur in publicly financed health care markets. However, even advocates of health service markets acknowledge that there are features of health services that make them more susceptible to market failure than are many other goods and services. The emergent, contingent, variable and uncertain nature of health care means that, 'unlike computers or hotel rooms, no clear product can be defined and its price set' (Light 1997). There is also considerable information asymmetry ('quality' of service is hard to define and measure, even for experts, never mind for individual patients, and providers tend to have far better knowledge of the quality of their care), few buyers and sellers of hospital services, and significant barriers to entry and exit, particularly in the case of hospitals.

For these reasons, both the internal market of the 1990s and New Labour's reforms were designed in ways that attempted to capture the benefits of market incentives while anticipating some market weaknesses through policies to shape and regulate the market. The expectation was that individual patient choice of elective care and well-informed commissioners, when combined with PbR, would encourage hospitals to compete for patients by improving the quality of their services rather than reducing their prices, as prices, at least for services covered by PbR, were fixed. The creation of foundation trusts was intended to give providers the independence and flexibility to respond to changing patterns of demand. The two regulators – Monitor and the Healthcare Commission – were to ensure that providers were managed in a financially prudent manner and did not skimp on quality. The aim was that, on the one hand, providers of all types (public and private) would compete on level terms to attract patients on the basis of the accessibility and quality of their services, and, on the other, commissioners and individual patients, advised by their GPs, would be capable of shaping provision to meet their needs.

Not surprisingly, the assumptions made by the proponents of the market reforms were not universally shared, and many parts of the reform package were extensively debated. A number of commentators questioned whether a greater choice of provider was really deemed important by patients, arguing that patients would prefer good quality local services (Fotaki *et al* 2005; Clarke *et al* 2006; Greener 2007).

Others challenged the fundamental assumptions underlying patient choice policy, particularly that patients are willing and able to be active consumers making rational choices (Greener 2007; Greener and Mannion 2009b). Greener, for example, argued:

> ... *choice processes for health do not operate in the same way as they do in other services – they occur in a social setting where the support of family and friends is crucial, and so, as a result, narrowing them to an individualistic process which does not take account of these factors ignores the importance of individual support networks that are so crucial in welfare.* (Greener 2007, p 256)

Similarly, drawing on a previous empirical study, Clarke concluded that people recognised that health services were 'not like shopping':

> *Such services were needed in conditions of distress or illness (rather than being pursued as a choice); they were viewed as fundamentally relational rather than transactional; and they had a public as well as a personal character – people recognised that services had to deal with multiple and competing demands with finite resources (and that some of those other demands might be more pressing or urgent than their own needs).* (Clarke 2008, p 251)

Others argued that the choice policy did not consider the potential negative effects of (more) choice on individuals. For example, patients might experience anxiety when faced with having to choose from a range of options, particularly if they did not feel qualified to make such choices or did not wish to choose for themselves (Schwartz 2004; Clarke *et al* 2006).

Other arguments concerned the nature of health care markets in general, and of the NHS in particular, which work to attenuate beneficial incentives and produce undesirable outcomes. For example, some commentators suggested that, in the NHS, patient choice would be limited by capacity constraints, and that increasing capacity (eg, by encouraging new providers from the private sector) could increase costs without improving efficiency (Fotaki *et al* 2005). Indeed the creation of spare capacity could reduce efficiency through stimulating supplier-induced demand as providers attempted to make financially rewarding use of their assets (Edwards 2005).

Another anticipated problem was the lack of available and appropriate public or professional information on the quality of care offered by different providers (Appleby *et al* 2003). Information on the quality of care provided by different providers is essential for informed choice and effective commissioning, but, in health care, providing information for patients, and commissioners, is a complex task. While information on waiting times is relatively straightforward, other performance indicators are more difficult to interpret. For example, does a high rate of medical errors indicate poor quality care or a good safety culture encouraging fuller reporting by staff? The provision of public information may also have unintended consequences. Suppliers may respond by improving performance only in those areas that are measured, by avoiding patients who are likely to harm their performance, or by manipulating performance figures (Smith 1995; Propper *et al* 2006).

Perhaps the primary concern with the market reforms was their potential adverse impact on equity, a key objective of government policy. Competition in other markets places a premium on information and mobility, thus privileging higher socio-economic groups (Besley and Ghatak 2003). It was argued that equity of access to health care would be harmed for two contrasting reasons – the offer of individual patient choice would be exploited more effectively by better-off, better-educated, lower-need patients, and the fixed (average) price payment system would encourage discrimination against more costly, higher-need patients.

However, others argued that the offer of individual choice as part of the reforms would improve equity since it would raise the quality of *all* services, not just the services used by the better off. Le Grand (2007), for example, suggested that the movement of as little as 5–10 per cent of users should be enough to provide an incentive for all providers to improve the quality of their services. He also argued that offering individual patient choice to all NHS patients would improve equity since it would make choices available to all rather than only those able to afford to pay for care in the private sector.

There were other ways in which market reforms could create inequalities in access. As Klein observed:

> *The logic of the new NHS model is, in short, that it is the market which will determine the menu of options available to patients: so, for example, it may reduce the options available in any geographical area if it leads to the closure of local hospitals or a cut in the range of services they provide. This raises the question of whether there are any balancing mechanisms that allow collective – as distinct from individual – preferences to be articulated.* (Klein 2006, p 234)

According to economic theory, markets create incentives for improving quality and micro-efficiency, but they cannot necessarily be expected to address the need for strategic planning. On the other hand, the continuing influence of the state on decision-making – inevitable in a tax-financed system where public accountability resides with the Secretary of State and thence to parliament – tends to act to attenuate market incentives. For example, the temptation for central government to intervene to reverse politically unpopular local decisions to close services removes the threat that a service might be terminated on the grounds of weak financial viability.

Analyses of the internal market under the Conservative government had suggested that it could best be understood as a 'relational market' (Ferlie 1994; Tuohy 1999). These analyses emphasised the socially embedded nature of the publicly financed health care market where social networks based on trust were used to manage the inherent uncertainty of health care and the interdependence of organisations. The persistence of social ties, manifested as so-called 'sticky' referral patterns and patient loyalty to local providers, also restricted the extent to which a fully functioning market could develop.

Conversely, it was feared that market incentives would eventually create an adversarial environment that would break these social ties, destabilising local health economies and inhibiting the development of integrated forms of care. Commentators argued that while market incentives might be feasible in the case of discrete procedures such as elective surgery, other areas, such as the management of long-term conditions, would require collaboration rather than competition to provide continuity of multidisciplinary care, and that the market as constituted by New Labour was poorly fitted for this task (Ham 2007; Roland 2008). Roland, for example, argues:

> *The greatest demand on the future NHS will be to provide high quality co-ordinated care for patients with multiple chronic diseases. Recent NHS initiatives have increased the range of providers in both primary care (eg, walk-in centres) and secondary care (eg, independent-sector treatment centres). This has the potential to worsen co-ordination of care – an area in which UK performance is already poor compared with other countries.* (Roland 2008, p 626)

Reviewing the evidence on the impact of the market reforms

This book aims to review the implementation and evidence of the impact of the English NHS market reforms introduced under New Labour up to 2010 to see whether the concerns of critics and the hopes of proponents have been realised. It considers the following questions in relation to each element of the reforms:

- What were the intended aims of the reforms?

- How were the reforms implemented?

- To what extent have the intended aims of the reforms been realised?

- Were there any unexpected consequences of the reforms?

- What are the implications for the coalition government's reforms?

The impact of the market reforms is evaluated in terms of their effects on the efficiency, quality and effectiveness, responsiveness and equity of health care provision. These criteria have been chosen to capture the objectives of the New Labour government as well as because of their bearing on the general criteria that would be used to assess the performance of any public health care system. Nonetheless the exercise is not an easy one. The above criteria are subject to different interpretations and can be measured in different ways (Baggott 1997).

Furthermore, the evaluation of specific sets of changes in dynamic systems such as the NHS will always be problematic for the following reasons:

- reforms tend to have multiple, broad objectives, making measurement of impacts difficult because there is rarely a simple 'bottom line'

- reforms are seldom fixed, tend to be 'emergent' and prone to be overtaken by other changes

- it is difficult to disentangle the effects of one set of changes from previous, overlapping and subsequent changes as system reforms are rarely introduced experimentally or with any concern for their evaluation

- it is challenging to assess the relative contribution of each of the reform elements to the overall impacts described

- the processes and impacts of reforms tend to vary depending on the local and service contexts

- reforms tend to be politically and intellectually controversial since deeply held values are often at stake and, as a result, the evidence is subject to detailed criticism and counter-criticism.

With these challenges in mind, the authors have identified and synthesised the available evidence, both qualitative and quantitative, relating to the reforms in order to assess their impact and try to explain how the reforms have worked (or not).

The book begins with a series of chapters dedicated to the individual elements contributing to the reform package: Pauline Allen and Lorelei Jones examine the policies to increase the diversity of providers and introduce foundation trusts; Judith Smith and Natasha Curry examine commissioning; Shelley Farrar, Deokhee Yi and Sean Boyle evaluate PbR; Anna Dixon and Ruth Robertson review the evidence on patient choice of provider; and Gwyn Bevan addresses the issue of regulation and system reform. Carol Propper and Jennifer Dixon consider the overall impact of competition.

However, the reforms were designed to work together as a package of interrelated policies. Therefore, in a subsequent chapter Anna Dixon and Lorelei Jones review the evidence from studies of how the reforms were implemented in different local contexts and in relation to different services. The two concluding chapters seek to understand the overall impact of the reforms, and what can be learned for the future from this innovative and radical period of change in England's NHS.

2 Diversity of health care providers

Pauline Allen and Lorelei Jones

Before the introduction of the National Health Service (NHS) in 1948, there was a patchwork of public, private and voluntary provision (Keen *et al* 2001). Since the establishment of the NHS, when hospitals were nationalised, most of the organisations providing health care to NHS patients have been state-owned. General practitioners (GPs) are a notable exception to this, being self-employed and operating largely under a nationally negotiated contract. However, a small proportion of the care of NHS patients, mainly in the areas of mental and sexual health, has continued to be provided by independent organisations, either profit-making or not-for-profit. Moreover, NHS hospitals and commissioners have used spot contracting (ie, *ad hoc* arrangements negotiated locally) with the private sector in order to reduce NHS waiting times (and the number waiting) (Keen *et al* 2001).

Over the past two decades, there has been a marked shift in government policy to introduce a wider diversity in the organisations providing services to NHS patients (Edwards and Lewis 2008). This was formally recognised in 2000, when the government entered into a so-called concordat with private providers (Department of Health 2000a). This allowed NHS commissioners to negotiate locally with private providers for a range of services, including elective surgery and primary care. The size of the private sector providing care to NHS patients was very small at the time: in the late 1990s the NHS spent less than 1 per cent of its budget on purchasing private care for patients (Keen *et al* 2001).

From about 2002, a more systematic approach was taken to introducing more competition into the NHS. As part of this move, there was an explicit decision to increase the diversity of types of providers offering services to NHS patients, including organisations from the independent sector (both for-profit and not-for-profit, so-called third-sector organisations). Most prominent in this policy was the nationally led process of procurement of a number of independent-sector treatment centres (ISTCs) to provide high-volume, low-risk elective surgery to NHS patients. In addition, a new form of NHS organisation, the foundation trust, was introduced, with greater operational and financial freedom than other NHS trusts.

The government also encouraged for-profit providers to supply primary care services, with the intention of increasing capacity in areas with an insufficient number of GPs, a process that saw for-profit firms and social enterprises gain NHS GP contracts.

In this chapter, we summarise the evidence about the process and impact of increasing the diversity of health care providers offering services to NHS patients. We begin by highlighting some of the concerns that were voiced about giving the independent sector a greater role in providing NHS services.

Concerns about provider diversity

The Labour government's view was that if NHS providers had to compete with private providers for NHS patients (or at least if they felt that there was a threat of new entrants), they would improve efficiency, quality of care and responsiveness to patients. It was also thought that new providers would be more innovative than incumbent NHS providers.

Proponents of foundation trusts saw the new status as offering the opportunity for the more rapid creation of new services, greater patient involvement in decision-making about services, and a more business-like and efficient approach to management. However, a wide range of concerns was raised by politicians and other commentators (eg, House of Commons Health Committee 2006; Pollock and Godden 2008).

Efficiency

Proponents of provider competition argue that it will stimulate overall efficiency in the health care system. Yet the literature on the economics of contracting (Williamson 1985) indicates that transaction costs can be significant and, if these are taken into account, may limit the extent to which competition can increase efficiency. A number of studies of contracting in health care have examined how and why these transaction costs arise (eg, Roberts 1993; Ashton 1998; Croxson 1999; Allen 2002). Health care has a number of features that increase transaction costs between purchasers and providers, notably the difficulties of specifying the quality of services and monitoring that quality standards have been met.

Some proponents of increased diversity believe that independent-sector providers are intrinsically more technically efficient than those in the public sector, particularly because of the profit incentive in for-profit firms. However, as Allen (2009) points out, efficiency gains produced by competition may be vitiated by the loss of donated labour, which may well exist in the public and not-for-profit sectors (Hart *et al* 1997). In services where motivation to serve others is important, and many aspects of those services are not measurable, it is not possible to monitor and enforce all aspects of caring. If staff work in for-profit organisations, this motivation to donate labour is likely to diminish, as the benefits of extra effort will ultimately be accrued by the owners of the business.

Quality

There was also a concern that providers with strong incentives to cut costs (such as for-profit providers) might reduce quality of care without commissioners being able to detect this or enforce improvements in quality through contracts (Preker *et al* 2000). In particular, concerns were voiced by professional associations and trade unions about the quality of care delivered by ISTCs. Some of these related to the use of overseas staff (made necessary by the additionality requirement; *see* the section on ISTCs below), which raised concerns about clinical quality (House of Commons Health Committee 2006). Disquiet was also expressed specifically about the effect on quality of care of introducing new forms of primary care provider as a result of changes in regulatory mechanisms and lines of accountability (Pollock *et al* 2007).

Equity

It was feared that giving autonomy to better-performing foundation trusts might compromise equity of access to the hospital sector: foundation trusts might expand their activities, reducing the funding available for other acute providers and for community and primary care; and foundation trusts might not co-operate with other NHS bodies, thereby compromising service integration (Mohan 2003; House of Commons Health Committee 2008).

ISTCs have also been criticised for their potential to compromise equity of access as a result of their being able to select or cherry-pick the more profitable cases because they were set up specifically to treat low-risk, elective patients rather than high-risk, high-cost patients (Bartlett *et al* 2011).

The introduction of for-profit providers in general practice has not so far been found to harm equity of access. However, where for-profit providers found it difficult to make a profit, or realised their business model was ill-fitted to primary care, they withdrew and closed their primary care clinics (Iacobucci 2009), leaving the primary care trust (PCT) to find other practices willing to take the patients. This could harm equity of access to primary care since for-profit providers tended to be established in areas with an insufficient number of GPs.

Accountability

The payment of public money to independent organisations raised concerns about a possible diminution in public accountability (Hodge 2000). It is more difficult to ensure that those in independent organisations making decisions about services delivered to the public (using public money) can be held to account for those decisions (Vincent-Jones 2006). The mechanisms for holding public-sector staff to account are well rehearsed, and include legal action, formal complaints procedures and elections. The legal status of contracted-out services militates against the effectiveness of many of these remedies (Vincent-Jones 2006). There may well be a tension between the entrepreneurialism encouraged in these supply-side reforms and the need for accountability (Groot and Budding 2008).

For-profit providers: ISTCs

The most significant type of new for-profit provider in the NHS was the ISTC. As already mentioned, care had been provided for NHS patients by for-profit hospitals before ISTCs, but this had been mainly on an *ad hoc* basis, determined at local level. ISTCs formed the first nationally planned programme of for-profit hospital provision for NHS patients.

The specific aim of the ISTC programme was to provide the extra capacity needed to reduce waiting times for elective surgery (Department of Health 2002b). In subsequent policy documents, the Department of Health stressed that ISTCs would also increase patient choice, introduce innovative models of service delivery, and stimulate efficiency through competition (Department of Health 2005b; Anderson 2006).

Implementation of ISTCs

The introduction of ISTCs followed a capacity-planning exercise in which strategic health authorities (SHAs) were asked to identify, in conjunction with their respective PCTs, what capacity was needed to meet the 2005 waiting-time targets.

The first ISTC opened in October 2003. Contracts were negotiated at national level, and initial contracts were for five years. A minimum level of income was guaranteed to providers (the contracts were known as 'take or pay'). Once contracts were agreed, the relevant local PCT was responsible for ensuring that the commissioned activity was used. The staffing of ISTCs was based on the principle of additionality, which required staff to be external to the existing NHS workforce. This was intended to help meet the objective of creating more surgical capacity (Department of Health 2002b). Initially, in recognition of initial market entry costs, payments to ISTCs were approximately 11 per cent more than the national tariff paid to NHS providers (Audit Commission and Healthcare Commission 2008). Sussex (2009) has confirmed that this additional payment was indeed required.

A second phase of procurement was launched in March 2005, incorporating a number of changes to the policy in response to concerns raised by the House of Commons Health Committee (2006). These included a requirement for ISTCs to contribute to staff training like other NHS providers, and changes to the requirement for additionality. With the exception of certain shortage specialties, NHS staff could now work in ISTCs and all NHS staff, regardless of specialty, could work in ISTCs outside their contracted NHS hours. Changes were also made to the funding arrangements. ISTCs were still guaranteed a minimum income, but the relevant PCT would only be obliged to pay for care actually provided to patients, and the Department of Health would pay any shortfall to bring the sum up to the guaranteed amount.

Progress with ISTC policy was slower than originally planned. In 2005, the Department of Health anticipated that ISTCs would contribute 15 per cent of

NHS elective surgical procedures (Department of Health 2005b). In fact, ISTCs contributed less than 2 per cent of total elective activity by 2008 (Audit Commission and Healthcare Commission 2008). In November 2007, low utilisation of ISTCs led the then Secretary of State for Health, Alan Johnson, to announce that six out of 16 phase-two schemes would not be procured. An existing contract was also terminated due to low use (5 per cent) (Department of Health 2007a).

In the summer of 2007, responsibility for procurement of ISTCs was transferred from the national to the local level in recognition of the need for procurement decisions to be aligned with local needs. Data published by the Department of Health in 2008 showed that 85 per cent of the elective work that had been paid for had been undertaken, but only 25 per cent of the diagnostic work (Department of Health 2008b, 2008c).

Evidence of impact

Evaluation of the performance of ISTCs is hampered by significant problems with the quality of data collected from ISTCs (and, to a lesser extent, from NHS providers). The Healthcare Commission found that the information collected from ISTCs was generally not comparable with that from NHS organisations. A follow-up report published in 2008 found some improvement, although patient coding was still poor for aspects such as diagnosis, ethnicity and the treatment provided (Healthcare Commission 2007a, 2008a).

Efficiency

There have been no quantitative studies of the technical efficiency of ISTCs, although there has been one study of the overall efficiency effects on the NHS of increasing competition, which appeared to show that competition has, in fact, increased efficiency among NHS providers (Cooper et al 2010).

A study using interviews with staff concerning the performance of diverse providers to the NHS (Bartlett et al 2011) identified a number of characteristics of ISTCs that *might* contribute to greater efficiency. The limited range of services these organisations provided (eg, routine elective procedures or diagnostic services), and their status as new organisations, meant that the management could specify efficient, streamlined operating practices and then recruit clinicians who could slot into this predefined system of care.

The market reforms introduced into the NHS were based on the assumption that competition would create an incentive for providers to become more efficient, but it should be noted that competition between different types of provider was only partial – different organisations provided different types of services, not all of which substituted for each other. For example, Bartlett et al (2011) found that, as envisaged by policy-makers, ISTCs only competed with NHS hospitals in respect of routine, non-urgent surgery. Nevertheless, they also found that some NHS providers had sought to mimic the more efficient operating practices of ISTCs (Turner *et al* 2011).

Quality

The only comparative study to date of clinical quality in ISTCs found no significant differences between ISTCs and NHS providers. Browne *et al* (2008) were able to compare 769 patients treated in six ISTCs with 1,895 patients treated by 20 NHS providers during 2006/7. The study involved patients undergoing various types of routine surgery, who reported their health status using several validated outcome measures. After adjusting for casemix, patients reported similar improvements following hernia repair, varicose-vein surgery and knee replacement in ISTCs and NHS providers. Improvements following cataract surgery and hip replacement were slightly greater in patients treated in ISTCs.

There have been two studies comparing patient experience in ISTCs and NHS providers, each using different approaches. First, a study by the Healthcare Commission (2007a) involved analysis of routine data, patient survey, focus groups, site visits and interviews. It found that patients in ISTCs rated their care highly (97 per cent rated their overall care as 'excellent' or 'good'). A number of variables was rated higher than in NHS organisations, including time of admission and no change to admission arrangements, involvement in decisions about their care, and the provision of information and explanations about their care. There were occasional difficulties in ensuring co-ordinated care where responsibility for care moved between ISTCs and NHS providers and systems for following up patients were not always in place and not always included in contracts.

More recently, data on patient experiences were analysed by Pérotin *et al* (2011, forthcoming). Analysing the 2007 NHS trust inpatient surveys and the ISTC inpatient and day case patient surveys from 2007 and 2008 using econometric techniques, Pérotin and colleagues found that differences in ownership between ISTCs and NHS hospitals could not explain differences in patient experience. They found that ISTCs provided better all-round quality, fewer delays in discharge and more comfort than NHS hospitals, while NHS hospitals were rated better on the information given to patients. However, these differences were entirely due to differences in the types of cases admitted by the ISTCs and the NHS.

The multivariate analysis found that older patients, and patients in some specialties, were more satisfied with care in NHS hospitals, and patients in other specialties with care in ISTCs, all else being equal. Overall, regression analysis found no differences in the level of satisfaction reported by patients on the basis of provider ownership per se once patient characteristics, state of health and length of stay, hospital specialty, the selection process of patients into either sector, and individual hospitals' characteristics were taken into account. The analysis was unable to identify which features of providers accounted for differences in patient experience, but suggestions included the qualifications held by staff, resources and equipment.

Effect on the local health economy

There is some local evidence that using ISTCs might financially destabilise NHS providers. The latter have expressed concern that diverting more profitable, routine work to ISTCs leaves NHS organisations with the essential, complex and emergency care, which they had previously been cross-subsidising with revenue from routine work (Bartlett *et al* 2011).

Patient choice

A key objective of increasing the diversity of health care providers in the NHS was to increase choice for patients. However, a study of GP referrals (Rosen *et al* 2007) found that in some areas this may not have been realised because of the nature of the contracts, which obliged PCTs to send all patients with a specific condition to the nearest ISTC in order to ensure that funds that had to be paid to the ISTC were used for patient care. Another study (Imison *et al* 2008) found similar results in one study site where the PCT had ceased efforts to shift services between providers after a local ISTC had opened.

Summary of evidence

The evaluation of the performance of ISTCs has been hampered by the absence of comparable data for NHS providers and ISTCs, and the fact that there was only partial competition between ISTCs and incumbent NHS providers. The lack of data, plus the fact that contracts with ISTCs have not been made public, has also restricted accountability in respect of various issues, most importantly value for money.

The sole quantitative study of clinical outcomes suggests that quality of care in ISTCs is as least as good as in the NHS. Patient satisfaction with care provided by ISTCs is high. Higher prices, coupled with low utilisation rates of ISTCs while guaranteeing minimum payments to their owners, may have wasted public resources and failed to deliver value for money from these contracts.

For-profit providers: primary care

As well as developing treatment centres for elective surgical care, the Labour government also encouraged new entrants into the NHS to provide GP services. One of the reasons for this was to increase the capacity to deliver primary care in areas with an insufficient number of GPs (similar to the idea of ISTCs increasing available capacity) or where no conventional general practice could be found to replace a retiree. Both for-profit firms and social enterprises entered this market (Ellins *et al* 2008). Davidson and Evans (2010) reported that, in 2009,

23 commercial companies had multiple contracts with the NHS, and were running 227 GP surgeries. Although most of these companies run fewer than 10 practices (and can be described as GP-led despite being for-profit because they are owned by GPs), there is a small number of larger firms with a sizeable portfolio of NHS general practice contracts. For example, two publicly traded companies (Care UK and Assura) run at least 12 practices each.

There does not appear to be any systematic evidence about the performance of these organisations, although Ellins *et al* (2008) reported that, in 2008, in cases where contracts had been in place for a sufficient amount of time to tell, PCTs were generally positive about how these practices were being run, and there was some evidence of innovative approaches to service delivery. On the other hand, both Ellins *et al* (2008) and Bartlett *et al* (2011) found that some for-profit primary care providers were finding it difficult to make a profit, as the business models they had developed did not coincide with the realities of service delivery, or the terms of the contract offered by the PCT were disadvantageous. Some companies entered the NHS market only to close their NHS primary care facilities after a few years (Iacobucci 2009).

Third-sector organisations

One of the important strands of New Labour's supply-side reforms in the NHS was the policy that, in addition to the corporate for-profit sector, commissioners should engage with new providers from the so-called 'social economy', including local voluntary groups, registered charities, foundations, trusts, social enterprises and co-operatives (Department of Health 2006a). These groups are collectively known as the third sector.

Third-sector organisations exhibit a range of governance characteristics, the most salient being that they are independent of the state and have social aims. Third-sector organisations can take a wide variety of legal forms, including limited companies, charities, co-operatives and community interest companies (Allen *et al* 2011b), and some do make profits. The difference between for-profit organisations and third-sector organisations is that the latter do not distribute profits to non-participant shareholders.

The New Labour government was particularly interested in the contribution of social enterprises, which it defined as businesses 'with primarily social objectives whose surpluses are principally reinvested for that purpose in the business or in the community, rather than being driven by the need to maximise profit for shareholders and owners' (Department of Trade and Industry 2002, p 7).

The aim of introducing third-sector organisations was to develop the entrepreneurial impulse within health and social care, encourage entry of new providers, improve quality and promote innovation. There are two reasons why third-sector organisations may deliver higher-quality services than for-profit organisations. The first is that non-profit organisations do not face the same incentive as for-profits to minimise costs (Hart *et al* 1997; Grout and Stevens 2003). The second is that where third-sector organisations are client-led, they find it easier to respond to clients' needs (Weisbrod 1988).

In 2007, there were about 35,000 third-sector organisations in England providing health and social care services valued at £12 billion, while a further 1,600 planned to enter the market in the near future (Department of Health 2007a). Most currently provide services in the fields of mental health, disability, learning difficulties or long-term care. The government showed special interest in supporting the entry of new social enterprises to the NHS. In 2006, the Department of Health established a Social Enterprise Unit, allocating it a £100 million investment fund over the four years to 2010/11. This was designed to stimulate the growth of social enterprises through access to start-up capital, business and legal advice, and training. The unit also launched a so-called pathfinder programme for 26 social enterprises to act as demonstrator projects. In addition to encouraging entry to the NHS of new providers from the third sector, the government also encouraged existing NHS-owned community health services organisations to transform themselves into social enterprises (Department of Health 2007c; Tribal Newchurch 2009).

There do not appear to be any quantitative studies comparing the performance of not-for-profit providers of health care to NHS patients with the performance of state-owned NHS providers. This may be due to the fact that, until recently, there had been limited participation in mainstream NHS provision by third-sector organisations. (Contracted services had been mainly in the areas of mental health and the termination of pregnancy.) Where third-sector organisations did enter the NHS market, this tended to be in the area of community health services, and the routine data concerning these services are very limited.

There is one interesting study of users' views comparing public, for-profit and third-sector organisations' provision of services. The National Consumer Council undertook a study for the government's Office of the Third Sector (Hopkins 2007). This did not include health services, but domiciliary social care for older people was included. The study found that older people thought that private-sector providers were slightly better at providing what they wanted compared with the public-sector and third-sector organisations. There was little difference between the public-sector and third-sector organisations, except that the latter were distinctive compared with public-sector providers in two ways: keeping their promises; and having staff who were prepared to go out of their way to help.

An evaluation of the social enterprise pathfinders in the NHS (Tribal Newchurch 2009) found that it was too early in their development to be able to tell how they were performing.

In terms of international evidence, it has been argued that, in relation to efficiency, the level of competition that all organisations face is more important than the ownership of the organisation (Sloan *et al* 2001; Eggleston *et al* 2006). There is no evidence in the health care sector that third-sector organisations are less efficient than for-profit organisations (Vining and Globerman 1999).

NHS foundation trusts

NHS foundation trusts were set up in 2004. They were conceived as a new kind of public organisation, still part of the NHS but modelled on co-operative and mutual traditions (Department of Health 2005a). They are different from other NHS trusts in two distinct ways:

- they have greater autonomy – instead of being accountable to SHAs and the Department of Health, foundation trusts are overseen by the independent regulator, Monitor

- they have different governance arrangements – members drawn from the public, patients and staff elect governors including the chair of governors, who is also chair of the board (Allen *et al* 2011b).

Foundation trust policy thus contains two mechanisms intended to improve performance:

- that the prospect of enhanced autonomy will motivate staff to improve performance

- that organisational and financial freedoms, combined with new governance arrangements that focus on involving patients and the public, will facilitate innovation and enable organisations to develop services that are more responsive to patients and local communities.

In the second point above, public and patient involvement is seen as a *means* of achieving improvements in performance. Public and patient involvement has also been proposed as an *end* in itself, enhancing local democracy or active citizenship (Allen 2006).

The focus of this chapter is on the role of foundation trusts in the creation of a more diverse supply-side to the quasi-market for health care in the NHS. Findings with regard to public involvement are addressed elsewhere (Allen *et al* 2011b).

Implementation of foundation trust policy

Foundation trusts were introduced in a phased manner. An initial wave of ten foundation trusts became operational in April 2004, followed by a second wave of ten in July 2004. By 2010, there were 131 foundation trusts in England, of which 40 were mental health care providers (Monitor 2010). The government's original aim was for all NHS trusts to become foundation trusts by 2008. The Department of Health maintained that all care would be delivered by foundation trusts 'with the implication that foundation trusts will merge with or buy out the remaining non-foundation hospitals' (House of Commons Health Committee 2008, p 45).

The coalition government's White Paper in July 2010 indicated that foundation trusts were to continue to be a key aspect of the NHS, and that all NHS hospitals were to become foundation trusts by the financial year 2013/14 (Department of Health 2010a). Later policy announcements have softened this tight deadline (Department of Health 2011a,b).

Evidence of impact

The evaluation of foundation trust policy presents a number of challenges. A conventional approach to evaluation would attempt to isolate the effect of foundation trust policy by making comparisons using performance indicators, either of organisations before and after gaining foundation trust status, or between foundation trusts and non-foundation trusts. However, in the case of foundation trusts, this is made difficult by the fact that achieving foundation trust status is contingent on demonstrating high performance. Thus comparisons may reveal foundation trusts to be better performers, but it would be inappropriate to attribute this simply to foundation trust status per se, as foundation trusts are a self-selected group of high performers (Marini et al 2008).

Process effects of autonomy

There is evidence that foundation trust hospitals performed better than non-foundation trust hospitals, but the better performance predated the change of status (Marini et al 2008). A joint report by the Audit Commission and the Healthcare Commission (Audit Commission and Healthcare Commission 2008) found that foundation trust hospitals:

- had business strategies focused on growth and the development of services
- had an increased ability to plan
- used their ability to gain access more quickly to capital investment to improve and develop services.

In this sense, foundation trusts were acting more autonomously, as they did not have to wait for permission to make decisions from other parts of the NHS. But this increased autonomy should not be exaggerated: foundation trusts were still subject to national targets (notably the 18-week waiting-time target), and these had a major effect on the way in which they delivered and planned services (Allen et al 2011a).

There was no evidence that foundation trusts were using their flexibility in workforce issues in significant ways, but concern was expressed about the size of unused funds created by generating surpluses (Audit Commission and Healthcare Commission 2008; House of Commons Health Committee 2008). This could have been reducing NHS funding available for other providers.

While foundation trusts were better performing hospitals in the first place, evidence also indicates that the *process of applying* to become a foundation trust improved performance. An analysis commissioned by Monitor (Monitor and Frontier Economics 2010) concluded that Monitor's decision to defer some NHS trusts from achieving foundation trust status on their first application resulted in these organisations revisiting cost-improvement plans, which, over time, delivered significant savings.

Quality

As far as routine measures of quality (such as hospital-acquired infection rates and waiting times) are concerned, foundation trusts were found to perform better than NHS trusts (Audit Commission and Healthcare Commission 2008; Monitor and Frontier Economics 2010). However, there was no evidence that foundation trusts were delivering a higher quality of care as a result of their status, as they were better performers before becoming foundation trusts.

Various studies (Healthcare Commission 2005b; House of Commons Health Committee 2008; Allen *et al* 2011b) found that having more freedom to make decisions at the hospital level led to improvements in services for patients. For example, foundation trusts were able to make quicker decisions on opening additional wards or operating theatres, and focused investment on issues that are important to patients, such as the physical environment and security, car parking and patient information.

As Allen *et al* (2011b, p 69) point out: 'the aim of providing good quality patient care (whether for its own sake, or because it would enhance the reputation of the foundation trust and attract further patients) was clearly articulated'. This supports the earlier findings from Mannion *et al* (2007) that managers were attracted to the autonomy of foundation trust status by the opportunity to provide more responsive services to patients arising from increased discretion over the design of services.

Impact on the local health economy

One of the main determinants of the quality of local relationships between foundation trusts and other NHS bodies was the past history of these relationships (Healthcare Commission 2005b). Foundation trust status did, however, have an effect (Healthcare Commission 2005b; Lewis and Hinton 2008; Allen *et al* 2011a). In cases where there had been a history of poor relationships, these were exacerbated by foundation trust status (Healthcare Commission 2005b). Allen *et al* (2011b) found that foundation trusts were concerned to protect their services and future income streams against other trusts. They were also keen to expand the services they provided, to the detriment of other trusts, although foundation trusts were still co-operating with other hospitals in respect of issues that would improve patient care.

The incentives for foundation trusts to increase their income, coupled with autonomy in decision-making, meant that they were not always felt to be acting co-operatively with commissioners (PCTs) about service developments. Where PCTs were trying to reduce activity to prevent overspends in the local budget, having a foundation trust as one of the local providers was reported to make this task more difficult, as the incentives on foundation trusts were strongly in favour of increasing their income.

Witnesses giving evidence to the House of Commons Health Committee (2008) also cited weaknesses in the commissioning function as the cause of many perceived problems relating to foundation trust status, including foundation trusts not investing their surpluses and the lack of shift of services from hospitals to primary care.

Moreover, their relationships with primary care were complex: in some cases, tensions arose from concern by foundation trusts that GPs would use their commissioning powers (under practice-based commissioning) to reduce the amount of work done by the foundation trust hospital, but, at the same time, there was an incentive for foundation trusts to market their services to GPs and maintain good relationships to ensure the flow of referrals.

Accountability

Unlike NHS trusts which were held to account by the Department of Health and, ultimately, the Secretary of State for Health, foundation trusts are accountable to their members, elected governors and the independent regulator, Monitor.

Early studies indicated that there was a lack of clarity about the role of governors in relation to the board of directors (Day and Klein 2005; Audit Commission and Healthcare Commission 2008; Lewis and Hinton 2008). This appears to have improved over time (Ham and Hunt 2008), but a recent study of the governance of foundation trusts (Allen *et al* 2011b) found that governors had mixed views about how well they were able to hold foundation trust boards and management to account. One issue raised in several of the foundation trusts was that the governors were excluded from board meetings and did not get access to board papers.

Summary of evidence

There is consistent evidence that foundation trust policy met the aim of enabling foundation trusts to develop services that were more responsive to patients and local communities than had previously been the case. Senior managers reported that foundation trust status enabled faster access to capital to develop services. It appears that foundation trust policy combined autonomy with an incentive to become more patient-focused.

The key problem with foundation trust policy relates to the development of stronger providers combined with relatively weak commissioning. There is a risk that the continuing relative strength of providers in local health economies will vitiate efforts to create a system where the planning and provision of local health services is led by commissioners.

Conclusions

Despite New Labour government initiatives to encourage diverse types of provider to deliver care to NHS patients, a large amount of for-profit or third-sector activity had not materialised by the time of the general election in 2010. Bartlett *et al* (2011) found that, in the small number of local health economies they studied, less than 3 per cent of the local budget was spent on independent health care providers.

The small amount of available evidence indicates that the performance (in respect of quality, in particular) of diverse providers was not inferior to that of NHS providers, and might be superior in some respects. However, the effect of new entrants on the NHS system as a whole remains an area for concern. The policy was implemented by New Labour in a context of record real-terms NHS financial growth. In the current context of substantial cuts in public spending and little or no increase in NHS budgets, any growth in the market share of one organisation is more likely to be at the expense of another organisation. This may result in some existing NHS organisations becoming financially unstable, and difficulties in ensuring seamless care for patients across organisational boundaries.

The attitudes and behaviour of commissioners are important factors, both in the entry and growth of diverse providers, and in how diversity of supply is managed to achieve high-quality care and financial stability for local health economies. The coalition government's plans to reform commissioning (Department of Health 2010a; Her Majesty's Government Bill 2011) are therefore important to the future development of the policy to increase the diversity of provision available to NHS patients. These plans include changing both the arrangements for commissioning health care and the regulatory structure of the NHS. PCTs will be abolished, and consortia of general practices will take over responsibility for most commissioning. It remains to be seen if these new consortia will have the enthusiasm and requisite skills to manage the commissioning of a range of diverse providers in such a way as to maintain financial control and ensure good-quality care.

Regulatory changes will introduce a more competitive environment in which the current regulator of foundation trusts, Monitor, will take on the statutory role of an economic regulator for the entire NHS. Further changes are envisaged in the way in which prices are set for all providers, and risk is shared among them, which will enhance the competitive aspects of the English health care system (Health and Social Care Bill 2011). Although the reforms are intended to create a level playing field, it is not yet clear whether the financial environment and the new regulatory framework will encourage more private- and voluntary-sector organisations to enter the NHS market.

3 Commissioning

Judith Smith and Natasha Curry

Commissioning is the term used in the National Health Service (NHS) to describe what, in other health systems, is usually known as 'strategic purchasing' or 'planning and funding'. It is concerned with decision-making about the health needs of a population, the services that might be provided to meet those needs, the allocation of resources to organisations or practitioners who can deliver such services, and the monitoring of services to ensure that they fulfil the standards set out in contracts.

The term commissioning is specific to the English NHS, and used only rarely elsewhere to denote health planning and purchasing (apart from in relation to the planning of major capital developments). There is, however, academic analysis (eg, Ovretveit 1995) that distinguishes commissioning from purchasing or contracting. Such analysis suggests that commissioning has a more strategic and proactive intent, seeking to influence and shape what is offered by health providers.

Woodin explained the more proactive and strategic intent of NHS commissioning as follows.

> *Commissioning is a term used most in the UK context and tends to denote a proactive strategic role in planning, designing and implementing the range of services required, rather than a more passive purchasing role. A commissioner decides which services or health care interventions should be provided, who should provide them and how they should be paid for, and may work closely with the provider in implementing changes. A purchaser buys what is on offer or reimburses the provider on the basis of usage.* (Woodin 2006, p 203)

How far NHS commissioning in England has been able to enact this more proactive role and provide a real, constructive challenge to those organisations that provide health care has been the subject of considerable debate.

This chapter uses research evidence to set out the balance sheet in respect of the performance of NHS commissioning under New Labour. We examine the development and implementation of NHS commissioning policy over the period 1997–2010, exploring the reasons for different attempts to strengthen commissioning, and assessing the impact of these changes in relation to equity, effectiveness, efficiency and responsiveness.

We root our analysis within the spectrum of commissioning from the individual (personal budgets and patient choice) to the national (highly specialised commissioning). We focus on commissioning by primary care trusts (PCTs) and practice-based commissioners because these were the two main forms of commissioning during the Labour years with responsibility for the majority of NHS resources.

The chapter concludes with a discussion of the lessons to be learned from the experience of NHS commissioning from 1997 to 2010 and reflects on what this means for the next phase of NHS reforms.

The purchaser-provider split

The separation of commissioning (or purchasing) from provision, often referred to in the NHS as the purchaser–provider split, dates back to the Conservative government's NHS reforms in the early 1990s. The theory behind this separation is that those who fund and purchase care (the commissioners) can concentrate on assessing needs, planning services, and ensuring that an appropriate mix of services is available for a specific population (Le Grand *et al* 1998). This split is predicated on a belief that health providers (hospitals, doctors, general practices, etc) have greater knowledge about health services than those who use them. A dedicated commissioning function is intended to help overcome this asymmetry of information with the commissioner (eg, the PCT) acting as an agent for the patient or member of the public.

Commissioning in the international context

Health care commissioning is something that is regarded as being very difficult to do. In a review of the international evidence on health care purchasing in 2000, Mays and Hand summed it up thus: 'Purchasing health services is inherently difficult in publicly financed health systems since purchasers are continually faced with the multiple and frequently conflicting explicit and implicit expectations of politicians, central government officials, managers, clinicians, patients and the public for the health system' (Mays and Hand 2000, pp 30–1).

Likewise, a major review of health care purchasing in Europe (Figueras *et al* 2005) found a significant diversity across European countries in how health funding and planning was organised, and noted that these varying approaches were the result of a complex interplay of historical, cultural and economic factors within individual countries. For example, some countries rely on national social insurance funds to purchase health care, others place this function within local or regional government, and others (like the NHS) establish specific health commissioning bodies within the publicly funded health system.

Figure 3 The continuum of commissioning at the end of the New Labour years

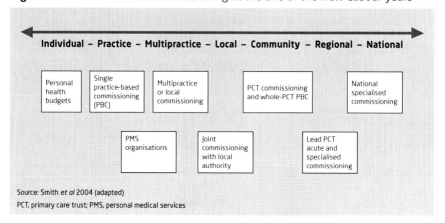

Source: Smith *et al* 2004 (adapted)
PCT, primary care trust; PMS, personal medical services

While some health care purchasing is best done at a local level (eg, primary care and chronic disease management), other elements will require a regional or even national approach (eg, very specialised hospital services and public health programmes such as flu prevention). There is no 'one size fits all' approach, but rather a need for 'levels of commissioning' (Smith *et al* 2004, p 22). A 'continuum of commissioning' (Smith *et al* 2004, p 5) has emerged within the NHS (*see* Figure 3 above).

The task of allocating limited resources to different services in a way that can maximise the health of a specific population, and assure appropriate levels of care and patient satisfaction, is challenging and yet important. Commissioning does not exist in isolation – it operates alongside (and within) the complex array of policy mechanisms within a health system.

Implementation

There were two main approaches to commissioning in the NHS under New Labour:

■ commissioning by PCTs

■ practice-based commissioning.

We examine both in more detail below.

Commissioning by PCTs

PCTs, the 303 statutory bodies (reduced to 152 in 2006) with responsibility for improving the health of the local population by using public money to plan and purchase health services, began to form from 2000 onwards. They covered all of England by 2002, following implementation of *Shifting the Balance of Power Within the NHS – Securing Delivery* (Department of Health 2001b).

They were regarded as the 'NHS Local' (Wade *et al* 2006, p 6) and brought together the functions of their forerunner health authorities (ie, public health, resource allocation, planning, purchasing, service review, primary care contracting) with those of primary care groups (ie, primary care-led purchasing, local planning, clinical governance in primary care). PCTs also assumed responsibility for managing community and other health services previously in the remit of NHS community health service trusts. The PCT model was predicated on a belief that strong local commissioners would be able to assume financial risk for a defined geographic population, providing community health services, and buying other services.

In 2008/9, the NHS operating framework (Department of Health 2007b) required all PCTs to create an internal separation of their commissioner and provider functions and to agree service level agreements with their provider arm on the same basis as all other providers. This separation was intended both to improve PCT provider services through more robust purchaser challenge, and to enhance commissioning by giving PCTs the opportunity to focus on their commissioning activities.

In late 2007, the Department of Health introduced world class commissioning (WCC), an initiative intended to bring about a step-change in the commissioning capacity and capability of PCTs. WCC set out a number of competencies that PCTs were expected to achieve (*see* Box 1 overleaf). PCTs' performance was measured against these competencies in order to track – and encourage – progress. PCTs completed the ratings process for two years (2008/9 and 2009/10). In each year, PCTs were scored for each competency. In 2009/10, an extra competency was added bringing the total to 11, and PCTs were also scored for three areas of governance (board, strategy and finance). In addition, a tougher assessment standard was used in the second year (NHS Confederation 2010).

Practice-based commissioning

The second approach to commissioning was practice-based commissioning (PBC) introduced in 2005 (Crisp 2005). Forerunners included GP fundholding, locality purchasing, and total purchasing in the 1990s (*see* Le Grand *et al* 1998 for a summary of the evidence on their performance), and GP commissioning and primary care groups in the early 2000s (*see* Dowling and Glendinning 2003; Smith and Goodwin 2006 for an overview).

PBC was set up as a voluntary scheme for GPs in which a practice or, more commonly, a group of practices, could ask their PCT to delegate an indicative (not real) budget to them, with which they would then plan and commission a defined set of services for the population of patients registered with their practices. Practice-based commissioners were, subject to the approval of the local PCT, able to keep financial savings in order to develop other local services and could pay themselves to provide such services, or buy them from other providers. This ability to 'make or buy' has been a feature of most forms of primary care-led commissioning in

Box 1 The 11 WCC competencies

The Department of Health document described the WCC competencies by means of a series of 11 headlines. These required commissioners to:

1. be recognised as the local leader of the NHS

2. work collaboratively with community partners to commission services that optimise health gains and reduce inequalities

3. seek and build meaningful engagement with the public and patients in a proactive manner in order to shape services and improve health

4. lead continuous and meaningful engagement with clinicians to inform strategy, and drive quality, service design and resource utilisation

5. manage knowledge and undertake robust and regular needs assessments to establish a full understanding of current and future health needs and requirements

6. prioritise investment according to the local needs, service requirements and values of the NHS

7. stimulate the market effectively so as to meet demand and secure the required clinical, health and well-being outcomes

8. promote and specify continuous improvements in quality and outcomes through clinical and provider innovation and configuration

9. secure procurement skills that ensure robust and viable contracts

10. manage systems effectively and work in partnership with providers to ensure contract compliance and continuous improvements in quality and outcomes

11. make sound financial investments to ensure sustainable development and value for money (2009/10 only).

Source: adapted from Department of Health 2007d

the NHS to date and has been regarded as offering the potential for GPs to scope new forms of better integrated services (Smith *et al* 2009; Lewis *et al* 2010; Smith *et al* 2010).

PBC took a range of forms (eg, individual practices, consortia of practices, social enterprise organisations), and research in 2009 (Wood and Curry, 2009) revealed that 30 per cent of practice-based commissioners were part of a cluster that had set itself up as a formal organisation. Evidence on the effectiveness of PBC is, however, equivocal, as we shall see in the next section of this chapter.

Impact

The 'weakness' of commissioning

Critique of commissioning under New Labour typically asserts that it was weak and failed to become a major driver of improvement in the NHS. An editorial in the *British Medical Journal* discussed whether PBC was the 'sick man of the reforms' (Lewis *et al* 2007, p 1168), successive Audit Commission reports have pointed to a disappointing lack of progress by both PCTs and PBC, and the House of Commons Health Committee inquiry into commissioning published in March 2010 concluded: '... weaknesses remain 20 years after the introduction of the purchaser–provider split. Commissioners continue to be passive, when to do their work efficiently they must insist on quality and challenge the inefficiencies of providers, particularly unevidenced variations in clinical practice' (House of Commons Health Committee 2010a, p 38).

The challenge of evaluating NHS commissioning

Assessing and quantifying the impact of commissioning is difficult, not least because it is just one of a set of interdependent reforms. The plethora of reforms implemented in parallel with PCTs and PBC make it difficult to attribute change to commissioning as opposed to other functions, such as performance management, payment systems or regulation. In addition, it can be difficult to separate the contribution of the commissioner from that of the provider in any service improvement.

Furthermore, the development of commissioning in the English NHS has been characterised by regular structural change. During Labour's time in office, each set of commissioning arrangements (eg, primary care groups and health authorities, small PCTs, larger PCTs with PBC) lasted only a few years, which inhibited longitudinal evaluation. Many of the objectives of health commissioning are, however, measurable only over the long term, the result being that where research has been carried out, it has necessarily focused on the structures and process, rather than the impact, of commissioning.

The result is that there is relatively little robust research evidence about the performance of commissioning on which to draw. Evaluations of commissioning during the 1990s were found to be similarly problematic (*see* Le Grand *et al* 1998; Mays *et al* 2001; Smith and Goodwin 2006), although the localised or pilot nature of some of those reforms (such as GP fundholding and total purchasing) offered the possibility for some analysis comparing populations served by fundholders and those not.

The section below draws together the evidence there is on the impact of commissioning over the period 1997–2010.

Equity

A core role of NHS commissioners is to assess health needs and commission services to meet those needs. This involves ensuring equity of provision and access to services for the local population. Indeed, the NHS Plan stated that PCTs would 'identify and maintain registers of those at the greatest risk from serious illness – concentrating particularly on areas where ill health is most prevalent – so that people can be offered preventive treatment. In the process the NHS will help tackle health inequalities' (Department of Health 2000b, p 18).

PCT commissioning and equity

The publication of *Shifting the Balance of Power Within the NHS* (Department of Health 2001b) signalled the devolution of new responsibilities for health improvement to PCTs. PCTs were given responsibility for 'assessing the health needs of their local community and preparing plans for health improvement which recognise the diversity of local needs' (Department of Health 2001b, p 13).

In later policy documents, PCTs, especially in their role as commissioners, were described as 'the most powerful agent to reduce health inequalities' (Department of Health 2008a, p 65). In this role, PCTs were required to undertake 'health equity audits' to identify how fairly services or other resources were distributed compared with needs in a particular area in order to identify priorities (Department of Health 2003b, p 41). They were also required to produce health improvement plans that outlined and co-ordinated activity to improve health and reduce inequalities within a local population. These plans were driven by a number of national public service agreement (PSA) targets designed to reduce health inequalities (*see* Box 2 below).

Box 2 Key PSA inequalities targets

The government's aim to reduce health inequalities was supported by a national PSA target:

- by 2010, to reduce inequalities in health outcomes by 10 per cent as measured by infant mortality and life expectancy at birth

The PSA target was underpinned by two more detailed objectives:

- starting with children under one year, by 2010 to reduce by at least 10 per cent the gap in mortality between routine and manual groups and the population as a whole

- starting with local authorities, by 2010 to reduce by at least 10 per cent the gap between the fifth of areas with the lowest life expectancy at birth and the population as a whole.

Source: Department of Health 2003b

In an attempt to focus effort on the most disadvantaged communities, a number of so-called spearhead PCTs were identified in 2004. Spearhead PCTs were the most deprived 20 per cent of areas in England with the poorest health indicators. A new funding formula was introduced that placed more emphasis on inequalities, and a National Support Team for Health Inequalities was established in 2007 to support local partners to reduce inequalities through evidence-based commissioning according to need rather than historic patterns (Department of Health 2008a).

A review of spearhead PCTs found that only 11 per cent were on track to meet the 2010 life expectancy target, although some other targets had been hit (eg, to reduce inequalities in cardiovascular and cancer mortality) (Pears 2009). This research concluded that spearhead PCTs had largely failed to narrow inequalities gaps, partly because commissioning arrangements encouraged a focus on annual operational targets and financial balance rather than on preventive public health. This is consistent with evidence from the 1990s that found that health authority commissioners appeared to focus on cost and activity levels rather than equity considerations, largely because of the financial imperative of contracting (Majeed *et al* 1994). In addition, the impact of the commissioning levers that were meant to be exclusively available to spearhead PCTs (ie, the additional intelligence provided by the National Support Team and Health Inequalities Intervention Tool), was lessened when these tools were made available nationally (Pears 2009).

A review of the performance of the NHS under New Labour reported that health inequalities had widened (Thorlby and Maybin 2010), and a review commissioned by the Labour government found that people living in the poorest neighbourhoods in England died, on average, seven years earlier than people in the richest (Marmot 2010). Although this review acknowledged that it was not simply access to health care that had led to such inequality and that wider determinants of health were important, it did suggest that commissioners should be doing better in procuring services 'that prevent or ameliorate the health damage caused by living… in disadvantaged circumstances' (Marmot 2010, p 154).

In 2009, a Department of Health review of health inequalities, found that despite an increase in overall life expectancy and a fall in infant mortality, health inequalities between different groups, areas and the whole population had persisted (Department of Health 2009c). Indeed, the recently published *NHS Atlas of Variation in Healthcare* (Right Care 2010) shows that there are significant differences across England in terms of treatments, expenditure and outcomes, suggesting that unwarranted variation exists with resulting implications for equity. The atlas states that those who 'commission healthcare have a responsibility to mitigate the effects of factors that influence poor access to, and provision of, healthcare' (Right Care 2010, p 13).

All this suggests that although there is evidence of improved health overall, PCTs largely failed to reduce health inequalities. Data from WCC supports this assessment. The average score for the relevant competency in 2009/10 – 'prioritising investment according to local needs' – did demonstrate an improvement on the score for 2008/9, but remained the second lowest scoring competency at 1.81 out of 4 (NHS Confederation 2010).

PBC and equity

The Department of Health saw PBC as having a 'pivotal role' in tackling health inequalities through GPs working with other partners to meet the needs of individuals and groups with particular needs (Department of Health 2008a). Evidence on GP fundholding in the 1990s concluded that this form of purchasing had, to some extent, created a 'two-tier service', with patients of fundholding practices having faster access to services (Goodwin 1998). The Audit Commission likewise warned that, if not managed well, PBC might lead to 'widening inequalities of provision and access between areas, as well as fragmentation in service provision, where some commissioners are more successful than others' (Audit Commission 2006, p 7).

No studies have looked specifically at the impact of PBC on equity. A survey carried out in 2007 revealed that few PCTs reported widening access or narrowing inequality as goals for their practice-based commissioners (Coleman *et al* 2007). Research into the impact of PBC did not comment on equity specifically, but it did find variation in the level of engagement and capability of GPs (Curry *et al* 2008). This research also found some indication that the size of the commissioning cluster had an impact on its ability to bring about change, a finding that echoed the evaluation of total purchasing in the late 1990s (Mays *et al* 2001). Although far from conclusive, these findings suggest that PBC was variable in its impact and that this may have had implications for equity.

Effectiveness

One of the main aims of commissioning under New Labour was to shift care out of hospitals and into the community, as well as shaping the provision of services to meet the needs of the local population. Although, as with equity, research evidence on the effectiveness of PCT commissioning is limited, there is a consistent finding that NHS commissioning has had a limited impact in shifting services out of hospital, reducing avoidable use of hospitals and developing new forms of care (Audit Commission and Healthcare Commission 2008; Ham 2008; Lewis *et al* 2009). Smith *et al* (2004) and Gillam and Lewis (2009) concluded that there was little evidence that any form of commissioning had had a significant or strategic impact on hospital services.

PCT commissioning and effectiveness

PCTs have been much criticised for their alleged failure to bring about significant change to patterns of service delivery, particularly in the acute sector and in intermediate care. PCTs were found to be weak in the face of strong providers with large and relatively long-term contracts. PCTs also had little direct control over referrals made by GPs, patients or consultants (Smith *et al* 2010). The relative lack of clinical expertise within PCTs was seen as a disadvantage in their ability to negotiate with secondary care providers (Curry *et al* 2008; Smith *et al* 2010), which arguably limited their capacity to respond to patient needs.

We have argued elsewhere (Smith *et al* 2010) that, although many of the criticisms are fair, the achievements of PCTs have often been ignored in the rush to categorise commissioning as weak, while not examining other aspects of the NHS reform programme that could be inhibiting PCTs from making progress. Achievements that PCTs have made include:

- working with providers to ensure significant reductions in waiting times for treatment

- the establishment of clinical governance structures and processes to assure quality and safety (National Audit Office 2007)

- the procurement of new providers such as GP-led primary care centres

- securing financial balance following a period of significant deficit (Audit Commission 2007).

Indeed, towards the end of the period, the Audit Commission described 'an overall picture of significant improvement over the three years assessed' (Audit Commission 2008a, p 4).

A survey of PCTs undertaken within the Health Reforms Evaluation Programme as part of a Department of Health-funded study of PCT commissioning revealed that a majority of the sample had commissioned changes to care in a number of disease areas (Sampson *et al* forthcoming). The most commonly anticipated outcomes of these changes to care were to be a reduction in emergency admissions and an improvement in disease-specific health outcomes. PCT commissioners in this study were mostly unable to quantify the level of intended impact, although there was some evidence of more sophisticated assessment of intended change in the final phase of the study.

WCC assessments in 2009/10 indicated an overall improvement in performance compared with 2008/9 (NHS Confederation 2010). The Department of Health did not officially publish WCC scores, although the *Health Service Journal* and the NHS Confederation published their own analysis. Improvements were particularly noted in the 'board' and 'strategy' elements of the governance ratings, while financial performance showed only marginal improvement. In terms of individual competencies, the highest scores were achieved for working with community partners, locally leading the NHS and managing knowledge. Improvements were recorded in each of the competencies, but the greatest improvements were observed for competencies that had achieved relatively low scores in both years.

The Care Quality Commission (CQC), the national regulator of quality in health and social care in the NHS in England, indicated in its annual health check of the NHS in 2008/9 that 70 per cent of PCTs fully met the core standards as commissioners of services, no PCTs were classed as not having met the standards, and 51 per cent of PCTs were 'full year compliant' for all core standards in their role as commissioners (Care Quality Commission 2009). No direct comparison with earlier years was possible as this was the first year PCTs had been required to make separate declarations to the CQC as commissioners and providers. Previously, PCTs had made one overall core standards declaration – in 2007/8, 21 per cent of PCTs were 'full year compliant' for all the core standards (Care Quality Commission 2009). These indicators suggest that steady progress was made by PCTs. However, such assessments tended to focus on the *process* of commissioning rather than its impact.

Despite some positive indicators of progress, most assessments of the performance of PCTs have been rather bleak. The House of Commons Health Committee (2010a) report on commissioning found that there were examples of good work being undertaken by PCTs, but concluded that many PCTs believed they were working more effectively than the evidence would suggest. For example, research into referral management found that half of PCTs studied believed they had been successful in curtailing demand, but quantitative analysis suggested that this was not the case (Imison and Naylor 2010). PCT commissioners have faced difficulties in shifting care from hospital to community settings. Analysis of admissions data in the NHS in England revealed an 11.8 per cent increase in emergency admissions between 2004/5 and 2008/9 (Blunt *et al* 2010). While not solely the responsibility of PCTs, this analysis does highlight the fact that PCTs have struggled to have an impact on emergency admissions.

The effectiveness of PCTs as commissioners has been limited by a number of factors that are explored in detail elsewhere (Smith *et al* 2010). One principal limitation has been the typically weak clinical leadership and engagement in PCTs in comparison with their provider counterparts. Capability and capacity limitations have also constrained PCTs, and regular reorganisations have led to a loss of commissioning expertise, which has then taken time to redevelop. PCTs have also suffered from a lack of autonomy when compared with providers (particularly foundation trusts), and information asymmetry has meant that providers are more powerful when it comes to the negotiation of contracts. This lack of access for PCTs to detailed information about provider services has made it difficult for PCTs to challenge provider billing and, in some cases, PCTs have lacked the skills to analyse this information (Smith *et al* 2010).

In response to the challenges facing them, commissioners increasingly turned to the independent sector for support with commissioning, and the use of such external support became the norm among PCTs (Naylor and Goodwin 2010). Research into whether the use of external support helped to develop more effective commissioning found that such support was not always used effectively, as a result of which commissioners did not always achieve what they had hoped for. PCTs with the greatest development needs appeared to be in the weakest position to use and benefit from the services of external organisations (Naylor and Goodwin 2010). This speaks again to the capacity and capability issues in many PCTs, as outlined above.

PBC and effectiveness

There is a stronger evidence base for PBC, but studies were limited by the fact that this policy was slow to get started and did not function long enough to enable a full assessment of its impact. Research by the Audit Commission, The King's Fund and the National Primary Care Research and Development Centre provides a helpful insight into how PBC was implemented (Audit Commission 2007; Curry *et al* 2008; Coleman *et al* 2009). However, unlike evaluations of GP fundholding and total purchasing in the 1990s (eg, Coulter and Bradlow 1993; Dowling 1997; Mays *et al* 2001; Propper *et al* 2002; Wyke *et al* 2003), none of these studies attempted to quantify impact.

Early assessment of PBC by the Audit Commission (2007, p 3) found that 'the redesign of services and their transfer from secondary to primary care had yet to gather pace'. This presaged the findings of a later study by The King's Fund, which found that many practice-based commissioners were more interested in using their budgets for small-scale re-provision of services within their practices than more strategic commissioning of services from other providers (Curry *et al* 2008). This suggests that PBC, as with its predecessor forms in the 1990s, seemed to be effective in developing extended primary care (Mays *et al* 2001; Dowling and Glendinning 2003; Smith and Goodwin 2006), but was much less effective in bringing about large-scale strategic change. Many practice-based commissioners felt they lacked the requisite skills to be effective commissioners. Key capability gaps were felt to be around data analysis, financial management and negotiation (Wood and Curry 2009).

A Department of Health survey, carried out in three waves at three-month intervals (Department of Health 2010g) attempted to explore to what extent PBC had enabled GPs actively to improve the quality of care available to patients in terms of better access, cost-effectiveness, choice, patient experience and clinical safety. The results indicated that the majority of respondents felt they had had at least some impact on each measure, although a relatively small proportion (up to 17 per cent) felt they had had 'a great deal' of impact. A perceived improvement was demonstrated over the three waves of the survey (*see* Figure 4 overleaf).

Efficiency

The purchaser–provider split introduced into the NHS in the early 1990s was intended to drive cost-effectiveness and productivity (Department of Health 1989). The more efficient use of resources remained at the heart of the commissioning

Figure 4 PBC group and independent leads survey - answer to question 13*

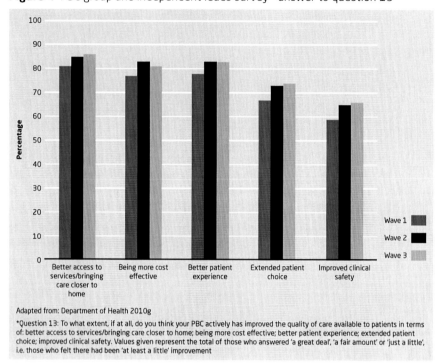

Adapted from: Department of Health 2010g

*Question 13: To what extent, if at all, do you think your PBC actively has improved the quality of care available to patients in terms of: better access to services/bringing care closer to home; being more cost effective; better patient experience; extended patient choice; improved clinical safety. Values given represent the total of those who answered 'a great deal', 'a fair amount' or 'just a little', i.e. those who felt there had been 'at least a little' improvement

reforms under New Labour and was included as a key criterion in the WCC assessment process (Department of Health 2007d). PCTs had a clear duty to commission services from providers to meet the needs of their populations without exceeding their financial allocations. Likewise, one of the key intentions of PBC was to improve the use of resources by providing an incentive for GPs to avoid unnecessary admissions to secondary care, either through demand-management or by developing services in the community (Department of Health 2006b).

PCT commissioning and efficiency

As with effectiveness, finding evidence on the efficiency of PCT commissioning is problematic as few studies have attempted to attribute impact to commissioning and then quantify this impact. Any analysis of NHS commissioning typically points to the need for commissioners to tackle un-evidenced variations in clinical practice as a way of making efficiency savings and delivering more integrated care (eg, Blunt *et al* 2010; House of Commons Health Committee 2010a; Smith *et al* 2010).

The Department of Health's atlas of variations (Right Care 2010) suggested that commissioners were not yet addressing such issues in a systematic manner. The House of Commons Health Committee report (House of Commons Health Committee 2010a) pointed to a lack of power among PCTs to challenge 'clinical norms' that might be inefficient. This apparent reluctance and/or inability of PCT commissioners to use data to challenge providers, and a reticence on the part of providers to be transparent about variations, emphasised the 'information asymmetry' that we noted earlier in this chapter as being a key challenge to all health purchasers.

It was expected that the biggest efficiency gains were likely to be made in increasing services provided out of hospital, both to prevent and substitute for hospital care. It is in this area that commissioning has most conspicuously failed to deliver (Audit Commission and Healthcare Commission 2008; Audit Commission 2009). One manifestation of this inability of PCTs to extract improved efficiency from the NHS is the failure of the majority to decommission services, or to assess their resource allocation priorities in a manner that entails root and branch (as opposed to marginal) analysis (Crump 2008; Robinson et al 2011). Robinson and colleagues suggest that PCTs' lack of autonomy limited their ability to make longer-term investment and redesign decisions, given that national short-term 'must dos' often conflicted with local priorities. This led these authors to conclude that PCTs only 'tinkered around the edges' of priority setting and rationing (Robinson et al 2011).

The financial regime in the NHS that has required PCTs to break even on an annual basis (see below for further discussion) has contributed to the difficulty faced by PCTs in making large-scale decommissioning decisions (NHS Confederation 2009). This annual financial cycle has also further exacerbated the power imbalance between PCTs and foundation trusts – the financial autonomy of the latter does not require them to break even on an annual basis and so allows them to make long-term investments and savings (Smith et al 2010).

In addition to a failure to yield savings, the efficiency of commissioning has aroused concern. The Audit Commission found that, in 2008/9, PCTs increased spending on community health services by 13.2 per cent but, instead of a corresponding decrease in spending on secondary care, acute provider trusts increased their income from PCTs by 6.6 per cent, suggesting that PCTs had made little progress in transferring care into the community or in dampening demand (Audit Commission 2009). In the same period, the number of inpatient and day cases increased by more than 4 per cent (more than in 2007/8), and outpatients by nearly 8 per cent (Audit Commission 2009). The Audit Commission has since reported that these trends continued into 2009/10, with inpatient and day-case activity rising, fuelled by less complex cases (Audit Commission 2009), and this is underlined by analysis of rising emergency admissions by the Nuffield Trust (Blunt et al 2010).

A survey of PCTs undertaken by the National Audit Office and commissioned by the House of Commons Health Committee in early January 2010 found weaknesses at PCT level in strategic planning, procuring services, and monitoring and evaluation. The National Audit Office found that commissioners had a poor understanding of costs and lacked evidence for the effectiveness of their commissioning activities. They also concluded that commissioners had a poor understanding of whether they had achieved value for money (National Audit Office 2010). The WCC score for the 11th competency (make sound financial investments to ensure sustainable development and value for money), which was added in 2009/10, was the lowest of all competency scores for that year.

In contrast to this evidence, researchers who have compared productivity in the English NHS with that in the other three countries of the United Kingdom – two of which do not have a purchaser–provider split – reached a favourable conclusion in respect of the apparent efficiency of the NHS in England (Connolly *et al* 2010). This report found that 'England has the lowest per capita funding for the NHS and makes better use of its lower level of resourcing in terms of shorter waiting times and higher crude productivity of its staff' (Connolly *et al* 2010, p 104). As with much of this evidence, it is difficult to know the extent to which that achievement can be attributed to commissioning in England compared with other factors, such as top-down targets, but it is nevertheless a counterbalance to the generally critical assessment of NHS commissioning in England.

PBC and efficiency

PBC is widely seen to have failed to challenge existing models of care and release savings (House of Commons Health Committee 2010a; Smith et al 2010). Research by The King's Fund into PBC, based on four case studies, found that the 'extent to which PBC was successful in improving the use of resources has not yet been demonstrated conclusively', even in sites where financial management had been a focus (Curry *et al* 2008, p 25). Where claims were made about savings, individual accounts differed and no empirical evidence was provided. The report concluded that it was unclear whether PBC represented a cost-effective form of commissioning (Curry *et al* 2008).

The findings of the other in-depth study of PBC echoed those of Curry *et al*. Some savings had been made by commissioners but these seemed to be mostly random or attributable to other factors, such as hospital reorganisation (Coleman *et al* 2009). The authors concluded that PBC had had a limited impact on demand for hospital care, with some examples of reduced consultant–consultant referrals, but overall that it had not been successful in challenging secondary care, again underlining a key message from previous research into different forms of primary care-led commissioning.

Despite this, Coleman *et al* (2009) are more optimistic about PBC than are Curry and colleagues, suggesting that there was still a future role for PBC in effective commissioning, cost reduction and quality improvement. They agreed that active engagement of GPs was lacking, but argued that this was not necessarily desirable, suggesting instead that this role should be occupied by a legitimised and committed activist sub-group of GPs. They also identified spin-off benefits from PBC, reporting potential quality improvements in primary care. PBC provided GPs with a platform for peer review in their prescribing and referral behaviour, allowing them to generate closer working relationships and ground-level intelligence to support PCT activity (the converse was true where GPs and manager relationships were strained, especially when efforts to innovate were prevented). These findings suggest that the PBC model had the potential to involve clinicians in commissioning and to raise standards in primary care. In practice, this requires the development of a shared process for priority setting and the establishment of a mechanism by which GPs could develop into commissioners for public health rather than simply developing small-scale projects at the margins of primary care.

Responsiveness

Commissioning by PCTs was intended to improve the responsiveness of services to the needs of patients, but a search of the literature failed to identify any studies on this subject. Department of Health guidance in April 2002 spelled this out thus: 'PCTs will want to use their local commissioning discretion to reshape how local health care services are delivered to reduce waiting times, increase responsiveness and improve clinical outcomes' (Department of Health 2002f, p 2).

Similarly for practice-based commissioners, guidance from the Department of Health exhorted them to: 'secure a wider range of services, more responsive to patient needs and from which patients can choose' (Department of Health 2004b, p 1).

PCT commissioning and responsiveness

PCTs had a duty to facilitate patient choice. The Healthcare Commission sought to create a 'choice' target against which to measure PCT performance, and to do this they combined data from the national NHS patient survey with data on the uptake of the Choose and Book system (the electronic hospital booking system through which GPs – or referral booking centres – can book secondary care appointments for their patients) in general practice. This indicated that PCTs made a slow start in enacting choice of elective care for patients. In 2007, 70 per cent of PCTs had failed to meet the target (with only 2 per cent deemed to have achieved it). The Healthcare Commission concluded: 'This is by far the worst level of performance for any of the existing national targets' (Healthcare Commission 2007b, p 49). Performance on this indicator showed some improvement the following year, with 39 per cent failing and 16 per cent achieving it (Healthcare Commission 2008d). This again points to some steady improvement by PCTs in relation to the processes of commissioning, and of attempts to embed a culture of choice within the local NHS.

Although PCTs were instrumental in establishing patient choice, this further limited PCTs' capacity to direct demand (Imison and Naylor 2010). Some PCTs established referral management centres, through which some or all GP referrals were channelled in an attempt to control this element of demand. There is, however, a question about whether their main focus being on assuring effective and efficient referrals was at odds with patient choice. Research into referral management schemes found that many were primarily intended to support choice and implementation of Choose and Book. Although this was the intention, few (24 per cent of the research sample) believed their scheme had successfully supported patient choice (Imison and Naylor 2010). This paper also found that referral management centres could create extra steps in the referral process, which could be confusing for patients who were unsure about the purpose of the centres (Imison and Naylor 2010).

Patient and public involvement is a key dimension of responsiveness. Commissioners are acting on behalf of the population they represent, and, for that reason, patient and public involvement should be embedded within their commissioning activity. WCC (Department of Health 2007d) sought to embed patient and public involvement in commissioning by setting out engagement with the public and patients as one of the core competencies against which PCTs were to be assessed. In relation to this competency, PCTs were required to 'proactively seek and build continuous and meaningful engagement with the public and patients, to shape services and improve health' (competency 3). WCC scores showed an improvement on this measure across PCTs in England between 2008/9 and 2009/10: average scores were 1.66 in 2008/9 compared with 2.35 in 2009/10, an increase of 45 per cent (NHS Confederation 2010), suggesting some improvements in this element of responsiveness by PCTs. However, a survey of PCTs in 2007 suggested that, although patient and public involvement was well established in the everyday business of PCTs, they did not (at that time) feel ready to involve patients in commissioning (Chisholm *et al* 2007).

Although some of the specific indicators of choice and public involvement showed some progress, public accountability among PCTs remained relatively weak (Thorlby *et al* 2008). Upwards accountability to the Secretary of State via strategic health authorities was strong, but downwards accountability to the public was weak, particularly when compared with local authorities which, unlike PCTs, are accountable to the public via elected councillors. The public had very little leverage over the local health services provided or commissioned by PCTs (Thorlby *et al* 2008). The general public had very little understanding of how local health services were organised or held to account – a survey commissioned by the Local Government Association (LGA) found that half the public did not know what a PCT was and three-quarters could not name their local PCT (Local Government Association 2008). This paper by the LGA points out that no organisation can be held to account by the public if the public does not know it exists.

PBC and responsiveness

PBC was introduced in recognition of the fact that PCTs were failing to produce the expected improvements in the performance of secondary care providers (Commission for Health Improvement 2004c) and in the belief that GPs felt disengaged from PCTs with little influence over commissioning decisions (NHS Alliance 2003).

One study that sought to measure the extent to which services had changed found it difficult to assess the contribution of PBC towards service improvement (Curry *et al* 2008). In some cases, initiatives had been rebadged as PBC-related when it was felt that these would have happened anyway. This study found that there were few examples of GPs undertaking systematic data analysis in order to identify need and clinical priorities, and the authors concluded that GPs tended to look at what they *could* do, rather than what was *most needed* for the delivery of better services to their populations (Curry *et al* 2008).

National guidance for practice-based commissioners stated that they were required to meet patient needs and to make plans available for public scrutiny, but there was no specific requirement for them to involve or engage patients in commissioning decisions. The guidance stated that PCTs needed to ensure that 'practices have engaged their patients in service redesign' (Department of Health 2006b). It might be expected that business cases would have had to include a commitment to patient engagement, but case study research found few examples of active patient involvement in PBC beyond consultations on specific redesign proposals. Where there was evidence, processes were not sufficiently developed to assess any impact (Curry *et al* 2008).

The third wave Department of Health PBC survey of GPs found that 86 per cent of respondents felt that PBC had enabled them to bring about better access to services to at least some extent (14 per cent of them 'a great deal'); 83 per cent felt they had improved patient experience (16 per cent of them 'a great deal'); and 74 per cent felt they had extended patient choice (10 per cent of them 'a great deal') (Department of Health 2010g) (*see* Figure 4, p 42).

Table 3, overleaf, summarises the key points presented in this chapter on the evidence of the impact of commissioning.

Discussion

It is important to note the limited nature of the research carried out into commissioning, and the difficulties associated with designing and carrying out longitudinal studies given New Labour's frequent reorganisation of NHS commissioning: the abolition of fundholding and establishment of primary care groups in 1999; the abolition of primary care groups and establishment of PCTs in 2002; and the merger and expansion of PCTs and the setting up of PBC in 2006. Indeed, some have suggested that the regular reorganisations themselves have limited the chances of commissioning achieving its goals (Dickinson *et al* 2006).

It is clear from our examination of the available evidence on PCT and PBC that the assessment by many commentators of commissioning as weak is, in many ways,

Table 3 Summary of the evidence on the impact of commissioning

Impact domain	PCT	PBC
EQUITY	<ul><li>PCTs failed to mitigate the impact of wider determinants of health.</li><li>Few PCTs focused strategic planning on reducing inequities.</li><li>PCTs achieved relatively low scores for equity-related competencies under WCC.</li><li>Spearhead PCTs failed to reduce health inequalities between areas and groups.</li></ul>	<ul><li>No strong evidence is available about impact on equity.</li><li>Evidence of variable capability among PBC clusters suggests variable impact on equity.</li></ul>
EFFECTIVENESS	<ul><li>PCTs failed to make significant shifts of care out of hospital and into the community, failed to reduce demand and failed to reduce consultant–consultant referrals.</li><li>External support for commissioning was not always used effectively.</li><li>Some positive examples of PCTs procuring new providers (eg, GP-led primary care centres) and establishing robust clinical governance processes.</li><li>WCC scores suggested PCTs made improvements in terms of performance over the two years measured (eg, in terms of governance).</li><li>PCTs played a role in working with providers to meet national waiting targets.</li></ul>	<ul><li>PBC resulted in some extended primary care and mainly focused on the re-provision of services outside hospital.</li><li>Few GPs actively engaged in, or led, large-scale strategic change.</li></ul>
EFFICIENCY	<ul><li>PCTs secured financial balance in 2006.</li><li>PCTs failed to challenge inefficient clinical norms.</li><li>PCTs largely failed to decommission services. Where decommissioning did happen, it did not result in a release of savings.</li><li>PCTs failed to increase provision of community-based services.</li><li>PCTs achieved low WCC scores for efficiency of spend and many had a poor understanding of whether they had achieved value for money.</li><li>England, with its commissioner/provider split made better use of resources compared with other UK countries.</li></ul>	<ul><li>There is little evidence as to whether PBC improved use of resources.</li><li>PBC seemingly had little impact on demand for hospital care.</li><li>Practice-based commissioners failed to redress the power imbalance between primary and secondary care or make significant changes to services.</li></ul>
RESPONSIVENESS	<ul><li>PCTs had weak accountability to the public.</li><li>PCTs were slow to offer choice, although their performance did improve.</li><li>PCTs struggled to involve patients in commissioning.</li><li>PCTs struggled to influence providers, partly because of their lack of clinical leadership.</li><li>There is a lack of clarity over the impact of referral management centres on choice and responsiveness.</li></ul>	<ul><li>Evidence suggests that GPs focused on re-providing services that they were able to do themselves rather than commissioning or providing services that their populations needed.</li><li>There is little evidence about patient and public involvement within PBC.</li></ul>

PCTs: primary care trusts; WCC: world class commissioning; GPs: general practitioners; PBC: practice-based commissioning justified. Along with other reform mechanisms, commissioning would appear to have failed to reduce health inequalities in England, struggled to shift care away from hospitals towards community settings, been unable to reduce emergency admissions, and been unable to demonstrate significant efficiencies or changes to funding priorities. When weighed against the transaction costs of running a commissioning system, the verdict would seem to be weak or at best equivocal. Box 3, below, sums up the conclusions of two previous major reviews of evidence on commissioning.

Box 3 Conclusions of two previous major reviews of evidence on commissioning

But why did these [NHS internal market of the 1990s] organisational and cultural changes not result in more demonstrable impacts in the areas we have investigated? Although it is possible there were significant changes, and the studies we have surveyed simply did not pick them up, this seems unlikely to be the whole explanation ... The explanation must, therefore, lie with the way in which the internal market was implemented. And here there is a ready economic answer: the incentives were too weak and the constraints were too strong. (Le Grand *et al* 1998, p 130)

There is little evidence to show that any primary care-led (or other) commissioning approach has made a significant impact on the way hospital care is delivered, except in relation to waiting times for treatment. This challenges health funders and planners to find more powerful and sophisticated ways of exerting required changes from health providers. (Smith *et al* 2004, p 3)

We must, however, take into account the interrelated nature of health reforms and the inherent difficulty in ascribing outcomes to specific policy interventions (Figueras *et al* 2005; Ham 2008). The weakness of commissioning in the English NHS may be a feature of factors such as:

- the Payment by Results (PbR) regime for funding hospital activity

- the power and constitution of foundation trusts in comparison with that of PCTs

- the lack of real budgets for practice-based commissioners

- the struggle to secure adequate specialist analytical support for commissioners (Smith *et al* 2010).

Evidence from assessments by the Audit Commission, Care Quality Commission, National Audit Office and Department of Health WCC Directorate suggests that PCTs were 'upping their game' by 2009/10, making some achievements, and demonstrating enhanced capability as commissioners. It is frustrating, therefore, that a further 'redisorganisation' (Smith *et al* 2001) of the NHS is taking place, leading to the rapid dissolution of PCTs and PBC, and the snuffing out – for the fourth time since the creation of the purchaser–provider split in England – of the potential for the longitudinal study of commissioning achievements and outcomes.

Tentative evidence about PCT commissioning points to systematic and potentially important changes to patient care (Sampson *et al* forthcoming), and analysis of case studies of innovation in commissioning (Ham *et al* 2011) shows how some (albeit an apparently small minority) PCT and practice-based commissioners were able to reshape local services to better meet local needs.

The critical question left unanswered by this review is why so few commissioners appear to have been able to make the significant changes expected of them and whether the costs of running a commissioning system have been worth the rather limited results, as measured by research evidence.

There is a number of possible reasons for the underperformance of commissioning during this period, including the following.

- PCTs' lack of autonomy rendered them risk-averse and unable to challenge effectively more powerful providers that had greater financial freedoms.

- The misalignment of financial risks and incentives meant that PCTs carried financial responsibility for referral decisions over which they had little control and this exacerbated their tendency to be risk-averse (Smith *et al* 2010).

- The voluntary nature of GP engagement in PCT commissioning put PCTs at a disadvantage when negotiating with providers, where clinical leadership and engagement were strongly embedded. Although PBC went some way to strengthening clinical engagement, it failed to provide PCTs with sufficient clinical legitimacy to be able to challenge powerful providers in an effective manner.

- PCTs generally lacked sufficiently skilled and experienced commissioning staff, and this was compounded by regular reorganisations of commissioning bodies (Smith *et al* 2010). Many GPs felt they lacked the skills and time to undertake commissioning (Wood and Curry 2009), and the lack of real budgets meant that the incentives for GPs to engage in active PBC were weak (Smith *et al* 2010).

- Commissioners had limited access to detailed information about referrals and lacked the ability to perform complex analysis of the data that was available to them. This limited commissioners' capacity to challenge billing decisions and to take strategic decisions.

- The dominant hospital payment regime (PbR) rewarded providers on a per case basis, potentially acting as a powerful incentive to maximise activity.

Commissioners were apparently powerless to counteract this. The complexity of 'unbundling' the hospital tariff, along with the absence of a corresponding tariff for community services, further restricted the ability of commissioners to shift care from hospitals to community settings (Smith *et al* 2010).

The next phase of reform

Given the relative lack of impact that commissioning has had to date, and the problems associated with trying to make strategic purchasing effective, we conclude this chapter by making an assessment of the prospects for the next phase of reform of NHS commissioning.

Some of the fundamental problems associated with PCTs and PBC should be tackled by the next round of reforms. Under the new proposals (Department of Health 2010c), we should see GPs along with other professionals – in the form of clinical commissioning groups – taking full responsibility for both the clinical and financial outcomes of their referral and commissioning decisions. This is intended to bring about stronger clinical engagement in NHS commissioning, improved alignment of financial risks and incentives, and reduced levels of bureaucracy.

It remains uncertain whether the new arrangements will achieve their intended aims; and it is unclear whether the new commissioning bodies will offer more of a challenge to dominant providers than did their predecessors, and whether they will be more effective at shifting care out of hospitals, avoiding unscheduled care, and providing more efficient models of care for patients with long-term conditions. A key concern is whether clinical commissioning groups will be able to develop (or have the resources to buy) the management and analytical support they will require. The experience of the use by PCTs of external support for commissioning raises questions about whether GPs will similarly lack the skills to use such support effectively.

Although the proposed arrangements may overcome some of the issues that held back commissioning under PCT and PBC, it should be acknowledged that clinical commissioning groups will be operating in a very different system from that of their predecessors. Unlike their experience with PBC, GPs will be managing real budgets, competing for patients, and accounting to the public and patients for health care rationing decisions. In addition, GPs will be taking on these significant new responsibilities at a time of unprecedented financial constraint. The question remains whether they will be able to meet the tough financial challenges while also grappling with their new roles.

Finally, will the government be patient enough to allow the reforms time to work? Successive reorganisations of NHS commissioning structures have impacted upon commissioners' ability to bring about real change. There is a risk that this trend will continue, preventing the new arrangements from bedding in and taking effect.

4 Patient choice of hospital

Anna Dixon and Ruth Robertson

Patient choice is not new to the National Health Service (NHS). The nationalisation of hospitals at the founding of the NHS made it possible for a patient to go to any NHS hospital with a referral from a general practitioner (GP). In practice, however, GPs made these decisions on behalf of their patients and, for the majority of the 60-odd years since the inception of the NHS, patient flows to hospital have reflected the referral behaviour of GPs rather than patient demand.

There was a brief period under the earlier internal market (1991–7) when GPs were limited to referring patients to hospitals with which the health authority purchasers had contracts. So-called out-of-area referrals were possible, but required approval from the health authority. In contrast, GP fundholders had the freedom to refer patients wherever they liked, but for only a limited range of treatments.

Despite the avowed intent in the White Paper *Working for Patients* 'to give patients, wherever they live in the UK, better health care and greater choice of the services available' (Department of Health 1989, p 3), GPs did not consistently involve patients in decisions about where they were referred to. For more than 70 per cent of patients, the choice of hospital was made by the GP, despite claims that they offered their patients a choice (Mason *et al* 1994). The evidence from this earlier period of market reforms was that professional judgement took precedence over patient preferences. The standard of clinical care, proximity and convenience were most frequently mentioned by GPs as the most important factors affecting their choices (Mason *et al* 1994).

In 2002, the Labour government detailed its plans to strengthen patient choice: 'Hospitals will no longer choose patients. Patients will choose hospitals' (Department of Health 2002a, p 22). This document outlined plans to offer patients on long waiting lists the choice of faster treatment from an alternative hospital. The programme was piloted for coronary heart disease patients and those living in London, and was intended to make more efficient use of NHS capacity and to reduce waiting times. At the time, a quarter of a million people were waiting longer than six months for inpatient treatment (Department of Health 2004d). The use of patient choice as a policy tool to address waiting times followed similar initiatives in Sweden, Denmark and The Netherlands (Thomson and Dixon 2006).

Evaluations of the early choice pilots in England found it was popular with patients, although this is hardly surprising given that these were patients who were having to wait up to six months. The majority of the cardiac surgery patients offered treatment more quickly at an alternative hospital took up the choice (57 per cent), and the majority of those said they would recommend the scheme (89 per cent). Patients received support from a patient choice adviser, and travel and accommodation for an accompanying person, although some patients found this aspect of the scheme less satisfactory (Le Maistre *et al* 2003).

The London choice pilot offered the opportunity to be treated more quickly at an alternative hospital to patients who were likely to have longer than six months to wait for one of a number of elective surgical procedures. The majority of the extra capacity was in new NHS treatment centres (separate units dedicated to elective surgery at NHS hospitals) and other NHS hospitals, with only 5 per cent going to private hospitals. Only one-third of eligible patients were offered a choice, but the majority of those did take it up (67 per cent). The evaluation found no difference in uptake between socio-economic groups and, again, the majority were happy with their choice (85 per cent) (Coulter *et al* 2005).

The impact of choice on organisations was less clear-cut, largely because of the incentives and structural capacity issues they faced. Another component of the London evaluation found a convergence in waiting times between hospitals, and that the waiting times for participating hospitals that exported patients because they were not able to offer them sufficiently fast treatment, fell more quickly in comparison with the rest of England in ophthalmology and orthopaedics, but not in general surgery (Dawson *et al* 2004).The evaluation also found resistance from clinicians. Although there was no financial penalty for hospitals that exported patients, hospitals seemed reluctant to lose them (Ferlie *et al* 2005).

The majority of the additional capacity in participating hospitals that received patients came as a result of investment in treatment centres. In 2000, the government announced its intention also to set up diagnostic and treatment centres. In the first wave, 25 fixed-site centres and two mobile units were procured from the private sector to provide additional capacity for routine elective surgical procedures, with the first opening in 2003 (*see* Chapter 2).

As the government rolled out the choice pilots nationally, it announced that from January 2006 all patients would be offered a choice of provider when they were referred for their first outpatient appointment (Department of Health 2004d). The initial phase of implementation required that patients were offered a choice of four or five hospitals at the point of referral. This was extended from April 2008 to include any provider on a national list – NHS or private – that had agreed to provide care to NHS standards at the national tariff price. This shifted the policy from being one focused on waiting times, where the main objective was to make more efficient use of capacity, to one with a broader set of objectives. Specifically, the government hoped that choice at the point of referral would, as part of a set of market-related policies:

- improve efficiency in the NHS by reducing waiting times and streamlining administrative processes

- make hospitals more responsive to patients' needs

- improve the quality of the service provided

- improve equity by opening choice to all.

The remainder of this chapter will review the evidence on the implementation and impact of patient choice at the point of referral.

Implementation

The Department of Health tracked the implementation of patient choice through a national patient survey. Six months after the launch of choice at the point of referral, this showed that less than one-third (30 per cent) of patients recalled being offered a choice (Department of Health 2007b). This rose steadily to 47 per cent in March 2009, and then stalled, with the number recalling being offered a choice in February 2010 standing at 49 per cent (Department of Health 2010h). The same survey showed that the number of patients who were aware of their right to choose before visiting the GP had gradually risen from 29 per cent in May/June 2006, to 54 per cent by February 2010.

A more detailed evaluation of patient choice in four areas of England found that, by January 2009, although now entitled to a choice of any NHS or registered non-NHS provider, most patients who were offered a choice said they had been given between two and five options, with the inclusion of a privately run hospital in only 8 per cent of choices (Dixon *et al* 2010a). Interviews with GPs and patients in the same study revealed that GPs often offered choice in a tokenistic way, rarely initiating a discussion of the merits (or otherwise) of the options available.

Although many GPs could see the benefits of the choice programme in theory, they often resisted the routine offering of choice as they felt that most patients were not interested in making one, preferring the GP to decide on their behalf, and that, in addition, they did not have time to discuss the options with patients (Dixon *et al* 2010a). In a qualitative study, Barnett *et al* (2008) found that patients did want a choice, but did not want to be active choosers, preferring their GP to choose on their behalf.

We do not know how many patients used the offer of choice actively to choose a provider that met with their preferences. Some indication of this is given in the evaluation by Dixon *et al* (2010a), which showed that 5–8 per cent more of the patients offered a choice travelled to a non-local hospital than those who were not offered a choice. However, some patients will actively choose their local hospital, and others will be referred beyond the local hospital without that being their choice, and so the authors noted that this figure did not quantify the total number of active choosers. It did, however, give an indication that offering a choice led at least some patients to attend a hospital other than the nearest one.

At the beginning of 2006, an electronic appointment booking system called Choose and Book was installed in hospitals and GP surgeries to allow GPs and patients to book their appointments online in the GP surgery or from home. Even before the Choose and Book system began, it generated a negative response from GPs: just over three-quarters (78 per cent) described themselves as feeling 'a little negative' or 'very negative' (Doctors.net 2005, p 7) about the idea of it, and 93 per cent felt that there had been inadequate consultation on the system (Doctors.net 2005, p 6).

Initial technical difficulties frustrated GPs who, under time pressure in their consultations, found they were often unable to log on to the system or that it crashed during a booking (Rosen *et al* 2007; British Medical Association 2009). They also complained that a lack of training made it difficult to keep up to date with the regular modifications to the system, and that the inability to refer to a named consultant (unlike in a traditional paper-based referral) broke the links they had established with hospital clinicians (Rosen *et al* 2007; British Medical Association 2009; Dixon *et al* 2010b).

The technical problems not only made GPs reluctant to use the system, but also damaged their opinion of the choice programme in general. Despite a target of 90 per cent of appointments to be booked through Choose and Book by March 2007 (Department of Health 2006c), and the inclusion of incentive payments to encourage its use, only half of first outpatient appointments were being booked through the system by 2010 (NHS Connecting for Health 2010). GPs were key to the implementation of this policy, and their lack of enthusiasm for the programme and reluctance to use the Choose and Book system meant implementation stalled.

Only 22 per cent of patients booked their appointment with a GP or practice staff on screen in the surgery. They more often received a letter with their appointment (34 per cent) or telephoned the booking centre (27 per cent), as some hospitals do not offer appointments online, due to technical compatibility problems between systems (Department of Health 2010h, p 17). The new system put more onus on patients to book their own hospital appointments, which inevitably heightened the risk of some referrals never being converted into outpatient appointments.

Two online information sources were available to help patients select their preferred hospital. The Choose and Book system listed providers by distance from the patient's home and gave an indicative waiting time for each. A government-run website called NHS Choices (www.nhs.uk) provided additional information for more detailed comparison of the facilities at different hospitals (car parking, accessibility, etc) and their performance on, for example, readmission rates, infection rates and patient survey results.

In addition, information booklets were produced by primary care trusts with information on the performance of local providers. However, much of the information available to patients was not necessarily relevant or presented in the most accessible format – for example, information on the performance of hospitals on the NHS Choices website was mainly presented at trust level, and might include four or five hospital sites. Furthermore, there was little information about specific conditions or treatments: other than for cardiac surgery, for which risk-adjusted survival rates for individual consultants are published online, there was no information available on the performance of individual consultants, although patients often said they would like such information (Boyce *et al* 2010).

Perhaps as a result of this, only 6 per cent of patients offered a choice reported that the booklet was the most important source of information in helping them in that choice, with only 4 per cent citing the NHS Choices website (4 per cent) (Department of Health 2010h, p 18). Most patients identified their GP as the most important information source when choosing (43 per cent of those offered a choice), followed by their friends and family (29 per cent) (Department of Health 2010h, p 18).

GPs reported that they distrusted the official performance statistics that were available to help patients choose, preferring to base advice on their patients' past experience at local hospitals and their relationships with individual consultants (Magee *et al* 2003; Rosen *et al* 2007; British Medical Association 2009; Dixon *et al* 2010a).

Taken together, this evidence shows that four years after patients were first entitled to a choice of provider in England, and despite the fact that half had ostensibly been offered a choice, few had had a meaningful discussion with their GP about the merits of the different options. A very small percentage had been given a choice of any willing provider, and only a tiny proportion had consulted performance information to help them choose. Nevertheless, there is some indication that a small number of patients did use choice to seek out care from a non-local provider. It could be that, either the threat alone of patients choosing an alternative provider, or a small number of active choosers, is enough to provoke a positive response in providers.

In the next section, we consider whether, despite implementation being incomplete, patient choice had an impact on the equity, effectiveness, efficiency and responsiveness of health service provision.

Impact

Equity

The Labour government promoted patient choice as a means of achieving greater equity in the NHS. Previously, the ability to access care more quickly than that available in the NHS had been restricted to those able to pay for private treatment, but, it was argued, giving NHS patients a choice of provider would, 'make the best available to all' (Department of Health 2003a, p 13). There were concerns that choice would, in fact, exacerbate inequities as more educated patients with the money to travel would reap the benefits of choice, leaving more deprived populations with poorer quality hospital services (Appleby *et al* 2003). However, Cooper *et al* (2009) found that the variation in waiting times across socio-economic groups reduced from 1997 to 2007, although they were not able to isolate the impact of patient choice from that of other reforms.

Policy-makers hoped that patient choice would improve equity by increasing taxpayers' support for the NHS and stopping the better-off from migrating to the private sector (Alan Milburn, cited in Barr *et al* 2008). Evidence from the British Social Attitudes Survey (Appleby and Robertson 2010) shows that public satisfaction with the NHS has been steadily increasing since 1997, and is currently at an all-time high of 64 per cent. These increases can be seen across all population groups. However, it does not appear that choice is a significant factor in explaining satisfaction, although waiting times, which choice was designed to improve, do have some association with satisfaction.

Finally, it was expected that competition for patients would motivate quality improvements in poor providers, benefiting patients in deprived areas where poor performance was often concentrated. Evidence on whether choice provoked quality improvement in providers will be considered in the following sections of this chapter.

So what evidence is there that the awareness and experience of patient choice differed between groups? Data from the national patient choice survey found that white patients and those aged 35–64 years were more likely to be offered a choice, and white patients were more likely to be aware of their right to choose and to get to the hospital they wanted (Department of Health 2010h).

However, this analysis did not control fully for respondent characteristics. A regression analysis conducted by Dixon *et al* (2010a) found that older, non-white patients and those with no educational qualifications were the most likely to think having a choice of hospital was important. There were no significant differences in who was offered a choice in terms of education, age or ethnicity. However, patients with degree-level education and those aged 51–65 years were more likely than younger patients and those with no qualifications to choose a non-local provider. Older patients and those educated to degree level were also more likely to be aware of their right to choose before visiting their GP.

Interestingly, patients who lived outside urban centres were also more likely to be offered a choice, and more likely to choose a non-local provider for treatment. This is consistent with the evidence in Chapter 6 showing that the largest increase in hospital competition in the 2000s took place outside the main urban areas.

When interviewed, GPs raised concerns that non-English speakers might be disenfranchised by the choice process (Dixon *et al* 2010a). Neither of these surveys was able adequately to capture views from patients with difficulties understanding English.

Discrete-choice experiments present patients with information on hypothetical hospitals and ask them to choose between them. This type of experiment was included in the evaluation by Dixon *et al*, in which one of the choices was labelled 'local'. Respondents who were more likely to stay at their local hospital irrespective of its other characteristics were those who:

- had no access to the internet

- had a low level of education (no formal qualifications or GCSE/O-level or equivalent)

- did not normally travel by car to their local hospital

- were living in cities and large towns

- were aware of their right to choose (Dixon *et al* 2010a).

This research confirms the findings of earlier discrete-choice experiments that found evidence of a social gradient in those prepared to travel to a non-local provider in hypothetical situations (Burge *et al* 2006).

Overall, there is mixed evidence on whether certain groups of patients were more likely to be offered a choice than others, although when controlling for other factors, less educated, older patients and those from black and minority ethnic groups appeared no less likely to be offered a choice than others. There is some indication of a social gradient in those exercising choice, and older patients and those living outside urban centres were more likely to do so.

Effectiveness

A core aim of the policy to increase patient choice was to improve the quality of services provided by the NHS. It was hoped that patients would seek out the 'best' hospitals, or at least choose the highest quality from among a set of options based on published data on quality such as hospital standardised mortality and readmission rates. In a market where prices were fixed, providers were expected to compete on quality.

A number of quantitative analyses considered the impact of competition on patient outcomes during the period (eg, Cooper *et al* 2011; Gaynor *et al* 2011), but these studies did not isolate the impact of patient choice from the impact of other elements of the NHS market that stimulated competition (*see* Chapter 6), such as per case reimbursement (Payment by Results, *see* Chapter 5), private-sector provision of NHS-funded care (*see* Chapter 2), and competitive tendering of services by commissioners (*see* Chapter 3). The question remains: did patient choice promote quality competition within the NHS?

As we cannot directly observe whether patient choices led to better outcomes, there are two main sources of evidence available to judge the impact of choice on quality. The first is whether patients said that quality was an important influence on their choices. The second is whether those running hospitals said that patient choice motivated quality improvements within their organisation. We consider this second point below under the section on responsiveness.

There is evidence from patient surveys that quality was important to patients, but it did not appear to be the most important influence on their choice of hospital. When patients were asked to name the single most important influence on their choice, being close to home or work was selected most often (by 38 per cent of those offered a choice), followed by personal experience of the hospital (12 per cent) and waiting times (10 per cent). Quality of care was the most important factor to only 5 per cent of respondents (Department of Health 2010h, p 10).

In a previous patient choice survey, patients were asked to select from a list as many factors as they felt to be important in their choice, rather than having to select just one as being the most important (Department of Health 2009b). In that survey, hospital cleanliness/infection rates was the factor most often cited as important (74 per cent of those offered a choice) followed by quality of care (64 per cent) and waiting times (62 per cent) (Department of Health 2009b, p 8).

Quality of care was also found to be important to patients in a more recent analysis of patient preferences in both real and hypothetical situations (Dixon *et al* 2010a). A choice experiment conducted in the north-east of England to look at older people's preferences for the time and location of cataract surgery found that whether or not a consultant performed the operation was the strongest determinant of whether patients accepted treatment at a particular provider (Lim and Edlin 2009). This could be seen as a proxy for the quality of the surgical procedure.

The evidence suggests that patients think quality is important. Although many patients are loyal to their local provider, some are willing to travel to an alternative provider to get quicker access or a higher-quality service in both hypothetical and real situations. If a patient has had a previous bad experience of his or her local provider, he or she will choose to avoid it in future (Dixon *et al* 2010a). There also appear to be some differences depending on the specialty and seriousness of the treatment required.

Efficiency

Another explicit aim of the policy to increase patient choice, especially in the early stages of implementation, was to improve efficiency by lowering waiting times. It was expected that patients would choose providers with the shortest waiting time and so bring about a better use of capacity.

There is some evidence from discrete choice experiments that, in hypothetical situations, patients choose hospitals with shorter waits (eg, Burge *et al* 2006, Dixon *et al* 2010a), but there may be a threshold after which waiting time becomes less important. In one hypothetical experiment, when waiting times were less than 10 weeks, they did not influence a patient's choice of hospital (Burge 2006).

In the patient choice survey, 10 per cent of patients said that waiting time was the most important influence on their choice of hospital, but this was the third most popular answer overall (Department of Health 2010h). In an earlier survey with a different question format, 62 per cent of patients said that waiting times were one of the factors influencing their choice (Department of Health 2009b), and in another study patients ranked waiting times as a 'somewhat important' influence on their choice (Dixon *et al* 2010a). The more waiting times reduced, the less likely patients were to cite this as one of the reasons for exercising choice.

Waiting times have decreased dramatically since 1997 (Thorlby and Maybin 2010), but it is very difficult to isolate the factors that have contributed to this decline, although it is likely that the setting of targets and strong performance management were key drivers rather than patient choice (Alvarez-Rosete *et al* 2005; Harrison and Appleby 2009; Connolly *et al* 2010).

Further efficiency gains were expected from the implementation of Choose and Book. It was hoped that this electronic appointment booking system would remove the need for paper-based referrals and streamline administrative processes within GP surgeries and hospital outpatient departments. By allowing patients to choose the time and date of their appointment, it was also hoped the system would reduce the number of patients who did not turn up to their appointments (Department of Health 2004a).

Despite some accounts that patients processed through the Choose and Book system were more likely to turn up for their hospital appointment than those booked via a traditional referral, there is no firm published evidence of this (Dixon *et al* 2010b). More than half of patients were not offered a choice of time or date for their appointment (Department of Health 2010h). The Choose and Book system made the process of referral more transparent, and standardised some referral processes (Dixon *et al* 2010b), but it is yet to remove the need for a paper-based system of referral, which is still run alongside it. GPs have been reluctant to use the system, and in 2010 it booked only half the appointments eligible (NHS Connecting for Health 2010). Hospital administrators often print referral letters from the system, pass them to clinicians to annotate and return to the administrator, who updates the system (British Medical Association 2009). This falls well short of the efficiency gains envisaged from a paperless system into which clinicians directly input and assess information.

Responsiveness

As discussed above, one of the main mechanisms by which choice was expected to lead to quality improvements was by prompting providers to pay more attention to what matters to patients, that is, to become more responsive.

While providers were gathering market information, such as on the waiting times and quality of other local hospitals, and undertaking analysis, such as of referral patterns, they did not perceive that there were significant changes in market share as a result of patient choice (Dixon *et al* 2010a). Any changes resulting from choice were likely to have been masked by the increasing volumes resulting from the requirement to meet the 18-week waiting-time target.

At least some of the service developments mentioned by providers were intended to make the hospital attractive to patients, particularly the upgrading of facilities, but very few were as a direct result of investigating changes in market share or market research with patients.

Dixon *et al* 2010a identified many other factors that drove quality improvements in providers (*see* Box 4 overleaf). Some, such as meeting national targets and the need to comply with legislation, were common to all providers. Other factors, such as achieving foundation trust status or mission-driven changes, varied by provider. The report concludes that patient choice had an indirect impact through reputation: a provider's reputation would be enhanced by taking action to improve services, and patients would therefore be happy to choose that provider or to recommend it to friends and family.

Other reviews of the reforms have also suggested it was the threat of choice and not actual choice that influenced providers (Audit Commission and Healthcare Commission 2008).

What impact did this have on patients' experience of care? Patient-experience surveys have been conducted regularly since 2002 within the NHS, but there has been very little change in the overall scores and the NHS continues to perform comparatively badly on the extent to which patients are informed about and involved in their care (Thorlby and Maybin 2010). There appears to have been a slight increase in the proportion of patients who said they were asked for their views on the quality of their care while in hospital – from 6 per cent to 9 per cent between 2005 and 2008 (Garratt 2009, p 98). This suggests that more providers are recognising that, in order to keep patients loyal and to maintain their reputation, they need to ensure that every patient leaves having had a good experience. However, compared with other service sectors, this level of 'consumer' research is probably still relatively low.

Box 4 Drivers of quality improvement initiatives by providers

The study by Dixon *et al* (2010a) identified the following factors as key to driving quality improvement among providers:

- choice

- response to actual switching by patients

- response to anticipated or potential switching (a manifestation of a contestable market)

Other factors

External/national
- national targets/objectives

- National Institute for Health and Clinical Excellence guidance

- international directives

- legal/statutory requirements

- requirements of national regulators (Monitor, Care Quality Commission)

- relative performance on national indicators of quality

Internal/local
- capacity to change

- organisational prestige

- professionalism/intrinsic motivation

- commissioner/GP demands

- historic service configuration/quality

- patient feedback (through surveys, complaints).

Source: Dixon *et al* 2010a, p 134

Discussion

The implementation of patient choice in England during this period of reform followed several pilots and evaluations and was given significant support. The government invested in a new electronic booking system (Choose and Book), produced advertising and marketing brochures to promote choice directly to patients, published comparative information on providers (NHS Choices), and provided incentives to GPs to offer choice. Despite these efforts, the evidence suggests that the overall impact on the NHS was limited.

As with the other market-related reforms discussed in this book, it is hard to untangle the impact of patient choice from the impact of Payment by Results (which was partly created so that money could follow patients, *see* Chapter 5) and competition (for which patient choice was seen as a key driver, *see* Chapter 6).

From the evidence presented here, it appears that patient choice has not, as some feared, led to greater inequities in access to care – indeed there is some (limited) evidence that differences in waiting times by socio-economic group reduced during this period. Despite concerns that better-off patients would be more likely to know about and exercise choice, those with the lowest levels of education valued choice more and were no less likely to be offered a choice. However, there is some evidence to suggest that older patients and those with no qualifications were less able to exercise their choice by travelling further to access care.

Consistent with previous research and the experience in other countries, although patients said that quality was an important factor in choosing, in fact few patients actually consulted published information about the quality of care when making their choice (Marshall and McLoughlin 2010). Patients continued to rely heavily on their personal experience, the advice of a trusted professional (usually the GP), and the reputation of a hospital – something that is constructed from a variety of 'softer' information sources.

The importance of the referring doctor has been shown to be critical in other systems with a longer history of choice of hospital. In one Dutch study, only one-third of patients had made their own decision about which hospital to be referred to, the rest had been referred by the GP and relied on their physician's opinion (Lako and Rosenau 2009). Asked how they chose, 14 per cent indicated that reputation was the main factor, while 17 per cent mentioned other factors, including distance. Many patients said that quality was an important factor when choosing a hospital, and were in some cases willing to travel further or wait longer to access higher-quality care.

These findings are similar to those reported elsewhere. For example, a discrete-choice analysis of public preferences for surgical care in Germany found that the degree of specialisation and experience of the provider was the most important attribute, with patients willing to wait an additional four weeks to obtain surgery at a specialised institution (Schwappach and Strasmann 2007).

More easily observed factors such as waiting times are important to patients, but their impact on choice may be diminishing. Whereas during the choice pilots, a high proportion of patients was willing to travel to an alternative provider to be treated more quickly (Le Maistre *et al* 2003), under choice of referral, only an additional 7–8 per cent of patients travelled to a non-local hospital when offered a choice, compared with those who were not offered a choice (Dixon *et al* 2010a). Waiting times were, by then, significantly lower than in the earlier pilot period, however, and the differences in waiting times between hospitals were smaller, with most achieving the target of 18 weeks from referral to treatment.

Despite the greater availability and promotion of information on differences in the quality of care between hospitals in the English NHS, patients are extremely loyal to local providers. This so-called stickiness has been observed in other studies, showing that convenience and distance may outweigh quality, reducing the likely impact of choice on the quality of care.

In Denmark, patients who refused the chance to be treated more quickly at a hospital outside their own county cited shorter distance, transport time and previous experience as reasons for being 'loyal' to the local provider (Birk and Onsberg Henriksen 2006).

In Canada, a survey of patients waiting for joint surgery found that the majority (63 per cent) were unlikely to consider changing surgeons to reduce their waiting time. Men, those with higher levels of education and those who had already undergone surgery were more likely to change. Those with a particular preference for a surgeon before referral, higher self-reported health status, and who thought the waiting times were acceptable were less likely to consider changing surgeons (Conner-Spady *et al* 2008).

There is little evidence to assess whether choice has had an impact on efficiency. The improvement in technical efficiency that was expected to be one of the potential benefits of the Choose and Book system was not realised, and although differences in waiting times were reduced, suggesting better use of capacity, these reductions cannot be attributed to the choice policy. Indeed, the additional capacity available in independent-sector treatment centres during this period (*see* Chapter 2) was not fully utilised, as many patients were not aware of the option to be treated by a private-sector provider and GPs appeared reluctant to refer patients to them.

Although providers were monitoring the demand for their services, they focused their efforts on attracting GP referrals rather than on promoting their services directly to patients. There is little evidence that the introduction of patient choice resulted in increased provider responsiveness to patients. A range of factors, including a desire to provide attractive services and ensure that the local population stays loyal, drove service improvements.

Perhaps most surprising was the geography of choice. Patients outside urban areas were more likely to be offered a choice and to attend a non-local provider. Providers were also focused on GPs and patients on the fringes of their catchment areas, recognising perhaps that patients and GPs in these areas were equidistant from several providers and were more amenable to switching their allegiances, whereas patients in towns and cities appeared more likely to stick with their local providers, perhaps out of a sense of loyalty and identification and also their greater reliance on public transport (*see* Chapter 6 for more on the geography of competition and choice).

Policy implications

Patient choice of provider began as a policy to reduce waiting times, but by the time the Labour government had set out its market-based reforms in full, choice was seen as a key driver of competition between hospitals. The objective of efficiency, ie, making more effective use of spare capacity in the system, was superseded by the goal of responsiveness, ie, making services more patient-centred, with the underpinning philosophy being that hospitals would improve the quality of care as they sought to attract patients and the money that followed them.

The coalition government has again put choice at the centre of its English NHS reform proposals (Department of Health 2010d). The view is that a combination of greater information and transparency about the performance and quality of care, plus patient choice (now supported by GPs with real budgets and therefore with buying power), will result in a more efficient and higher-quality service (*see* Chapter 10 for a fuller discussion of the coalition's proposals to extend New Labour's market reforms). However, as long as GPs remain reluctant routinely to offer patients a choice, it is unlikely that policy commitments to expand patient choice will be realised. If patients remain loyal to local NHS providers despite the government's extension of the any willing provider market from elective care to other services, there are unlikely to be significant changes in market share and therefore few attractive opportunities for new entrants.

Under greater pressure to maintain financial viability, hospitals will be interested in maintaining activity levels and might therefore be keen to ensure that local GPs and patients view them positively. Guarding their reputation for quality may well act as a spur to improvement. It will certainly mean that hospitals will be eager to avoid scandals or public humiliation (such as by being listed towards the bottom of rankings and league tables). Given the evidence that patient loyalty is largely based on a positive personal experience, providers that want to thrive will make sure that every patient leaves having had a good experience and wanting to recommend their hospital.

While there is probably no going back on choice – the experience of other countries where patients are used to exercising choice suggests that they will not want it restricted – the evidence summarised here suggests that policy-makers should not rely on patients alone to drive quality improvement.

5 Payment by Results

Shelley Farrar, Deokhee Yi and Sean Boyle

There is a wide range of mechanisms that can be used to pay for hospital care. In the United Kingdom, hospitals have historically been paid a fixed budget based on the previous years' costs and activity, sometimes adjusted for planned changes in services (Raftery *et al* 1996). During the first internal market in the 1990s, purchasers mostly used block contracts – a negotiated amount that was paid regardless of volume, although there was some room to renegotiate the terms following delivery of the services – or cost and volume contracts, which paid an amount regardless of activity up to a threshold, and then paid in relation to activity above that level.

Payment by Results (PbR), an activity-driven payment system, was introduced into the English National Health Service (NHS) in 2003/4. It constituted a major change in the financing of hospitals, and introduced a set of incentives that had hitherto not been employed in the hospital sector in England. PbR made a direct link between hospital income and the number and casemix of patients treated.

Similar activity-based mechanisms are widely used in Europe and elsewhere in the world. Medicare in the United States pioneered this approach to hospital financing based on the costs associated with predefined groups of diagnoses and treatments. These groups are known internationally as diagnosis-related groups (DRGs). There are many national variations in the construction of such groupings. The version used in England is known as healthcare resource groups (HRGs).

The structure of the financing mechanism for hospitals affects their behaviour in a number of ways, such as, in terms of how they supply services, what and how much they supply, the cost of services, and the quality of services. At first, the aim of PbR, as a prospective-payment system, was to encourage cost-control and increase activity levels. In 2009, these goals were revised to reflect the Department of Health's aims to incentivise providers to maximise efficiency, improve quality, and shift care outside the hospital, as well as not to reward poor quality or unsafe care.

In this chapter, we outline the different ways in which hospitals can be paid, and discuss what impact we might expect a prospective casemix-based payment system such as PbR to have, drawing on similar experiences in other countries and English evidence. We start by describing the original policy objectives of PbR (and how these have evolved), its implementation and its development. We then consider whether the objectives of the policy were reasonable given existing international evidence, and summarise the evidence on the impact of PbR. To conclude, we consider the overall effects of PbR and whether the policy has met its objectives.

Objectives

It is useful to consider hospital payment systems along two dimensions. The first dimension is whether the price the hospital is paid is set prospectively or retrospectively. The second dimension is the extent to which reimbursement is linked to the level of activity, ie, whether hospitals are paid a fixed sum for a range of services or whether the funding is activity-based.

Retrospective-payment systems are rarely used today because they do not encourage hospitals to control costs or output. Fixed global budgets based on historical activity are no longer used to pay for NHS hospital care in England. In Scotland, Wales and Northern Ireland, NHS hospital funding levels are related to planned or expected levels of activity. In Scotland, for instance, there are no payments to hospitals for the treatment of individual patients. Global budgets continue to be used in many Organisation for Economic Co-operation and Development countries. For instance, the majority of hospital services in Denmark and the Czech Republic are funded in this way.

When budgets are fixed in advance of the services being provided, there is an incentive for providers to control costs, as they must remain within budget. However, there is no incentive to increase output as the sum paid will not increase with increases in activity.

In the English NHS prior to PbR, providers were able to negotiate for additional payment if their costs or output were higher than previously agreed levels. Under PbR, hospitals are no longer able to negotiate for higher payment. Although there is a local adjustment to the tariff (see below), it is centrally determined and non-negotiable for the individual hospital. The price paid per unit of activity is fixed in advance, giving an incentive for the hospital to control unit costs. If costs of an additional unit of activity are less than the price paid, there can also be an incentive for the hospital to provide more care.

The key document that introduced PbR policy was *Reforming NHS Financial Flows* (Department of Health 2002e). It identified three main objectives in introducing a standard price tariff:

- to enable primary care trust (PCT) commissioners to focus on the quality and volume of services provided (in the absence of price negotiations)
- to incentivise NHS trusts to manage costs efficiently
- to create greater transparency and planning certainty in the system.

The Department of Health expected the introduction of PbR to encourage cost-control and increase activity, and, when combined with other concurrent English health care reforms, such as patient choice and practice-based commissioning (PBC), to mitigate the possible negative impact on quality (so-called skimping) that is often associated with prospective case-based payment systems.

The Audit Commission (2008b) saw the main aims of PbR to be:

- to enable faster access to more appropriate, patient-responsive services

- to drive efficiency

- to enable commissioners and providers to focus on quality

- to ensure fairness and transparency of funding.

By 2009, the Department of Health (2009a) had revised its aims for a tariff-based system. These were to incentivise providers to:

- maximise efficiency

- offer the highest quality care

- shift care out of hospital settings

- not provide poor quality or unsafe care.

Implementation

PbR was introduced in 2003/4 for elective care in foundation trusts only. Prices were set for elective care based on average costs within the NHS. The intention was to move, over time, to a system in which all NHS activity would be commissioned against a standard tariff using HRGs or other appropriate measures that differentiated activity according to casemix.

By 2006/7, the tariff had been extended across all NHS providers, to cover admitted patient care and attendance at and treatment in outpatient clinics and accident and emergency (A&E) departments. However, even within the acute hospital sector, some activities remained outside the PbR structure.

Since then, progress to extend the system has been slow, with a number of major services still not being incorporated, including critical care, mental health care (which is discussed below), community health services, ambulance services and primary care. In 2009/10, only £26 billion of English NHS activity, out of a total of £103 billion, was paid for under PbR (House of Commons Health Committee 2010b).

In order to give providers time to adjust to the new national tariff, which would have resulted in many of them receiving less income than their actual costs, PbR was implemented in a phased manner. Similarly, many PCTs had to pay a higher price than they previously had and needed time to adjust. The Department of Health set up transitional arrangements in which gains and losses were mitigated over a period of four years. These protections were phased out gradually so that by 2008/9 the full PbR tariff structure applied.

The 2010/11 national tariff for admitted patient care, outpatient procedures and outpatient consultations was based on 2007/8 NHS reference costs (Department of Health 2010f). The 2010/11 national tariff for A&E is based on earlier reference costs (HRG 3.2) updated to reflect increased costs in A&E since 2009/10. With this exception, a general uplift has been applied to the tariff each year reflecting assumptions about price pressures. Thus, between 2007/8 and 2008/9 the increase was 2.3 per cent, between 2008/9 and 2009/10 it was 1.7 per cent. However, between 2009/10 and 2010/11 there was no increase as it was assumed that pay and other pressures would be met by efficiency gains as the NHS entered a period of major financial stringency.

The national tariff is also adjusted by a market forces factor (MFF) to account for unavoidable differences in costs across different parts of the country (eg, regional variation in wages and other costs of service delivery). As a result of the application of the MFF in 2010/11, there was a difference in tariff of up to 32 per cent between the hospital with the lowest and that with the highest MFF.

Structure of the tariffs

Admitted patient care

Admitted patient care consists of elective treatments (known as an ordinary admission if the patient is admitted for an overnight stay, or as a day case if not) and non-elective treatments – mainly emergency and maternity services. Tariffs are based on HRG spells.

In 2009/10, separate tariffs were introduced for admitted patient care involving an overnight stay and those not (ie, day cases), but this was changed back to a combined tariff in 2010/11, although separate day case and ordinary elective tariffs remain in a few cases. Tariffs are based on the weighted average costs of spells. These include all clinical costs (eg, costs of diagnostics and monitoring interventions), and all non-clinical costs (eg, capital charges, food, cleaning and maintenance). In 2010/11, there were 1,056 elective tariffs and 1,074 non-elective tariffs. In the same period, the tariff for different HRGs for elective care ranged from £161 to £33,531, with a median price of £1,416. For non-elective care, the range was also from £161 to £33,531 with a median price of £2,294.

A number of adjustments are then made to these tariffs, key among which are emergency tariff adjustments, long-stay payments, top-ups for specialised services and, most recently, best-practice payments – an extra payment for treatments demonstrably in line with evidence.

Outpatient attendances and procedures

Outpatient tariffs are set at specialty level for first and follow-up attendances, which may take place in a hospital or in an outreach clinic. There are 47 specialty tariffs, and these are based on the specialty of the consultant responsible for the outpatient clinic. For 2010/11, these ranged in price from £121 to £437 for first attendance, and from £63 to £348 for follow-up attendance. No national tariff has been set for non-consultant-led outpatient attendances, eg, those led by nurses or physiotherapists. In addition, for multi-professional consultations, separate tariffs are applied in each case.

The tariff has been structured to load the payment towards the first attendance so as to provide a financial incentive to minimise follow-ups. There are also HRG tariffs for 49 procedures that may be carried out in an outpatient clinic, replacing the outpatient tariff in those instances. In 2010/11, these ranged in price from £117 to £308. In all cases, these were considerably less than the equivalent admitted-patient care tariff.

A&E attendances

A&E tariffs are set at three levels: high, standard and minor. High relates to the use of high-cost investigations and imaging; standard to low-cost investigations or if the patient is dead on arrival; and minor to cases where there is no investigation, or where the patient attends a non-24-hour A&E unit or a minor injury unit (MIU).

Prior to 2006/7, the lowest level applied only to MIUs, but in that year a combined minor A&E and MIU tariff was introduced that reflected the average cost of minor attendances at A&E departments and attendances at MIUs. Attendances are costed at the same rate whether a patient is admitted or not. In 2010/11, the A&E tariffs for minor, standard and high activities were £59, £87 and £117, respectively. Although the Department of Health stated an intention to include attendances at primary health care walk-in centres in the PbR structure, this has yet to happen.

Unbundling care pathways

HRGs are one way of taking account of the very different types and quantities of activity that may constitute treatment for different medical conditions. However, each HRG can be disaggregated further into a combination of different elements of the care delivered (frequently called the care pathway) that drives that particular treatment. Known as unbundling HRGs, it breaks the care pathway into distinct components (eg, diagnostic imaging, rehabilitation) that can often be delivered in different ways and in different settings.

The Department of Health has tried to encourage the unbundling of care pathways so that commissioning and payment can reflect the fact that care can be delivered in a multitude of different settings apart from acute hospitals. However, unbundling has not been a mandatory part of the PbR structure. Thus, unbundled HRGs were introduced in 2009/10 for the rehabilitation element of care for a small number of HRGs (stroke, pneumonia, hip replacement, and fragility hip fracture) to encourage care to be delivered outside hospitals whenever possible. The tariffs for the rehabilitation phase in 2010/11 ranged from 42 per cent to 94 per cent of the full tariffs, but use of these is not mandatory.

Another area in which unbundling has been applied is that of diagnostic imaging within outpatient consultations. In 2009/10, non-mandatory prices were introduced for this part of the outpatient consultation pathway. However, these were withdrawn in 2010/11 on the basis that separate pricing of imaging did not provide an incentive for providers to keep the number of images requested to a minimum. On the other hand, non-mandatory indicative prices were published in 2010/11 for directly accessed imaging (eg, those requested by a GP).

Impact of casemix-based funding

There is a large literature documenting the design, implementation and, in some cases, the impact of casemix-based payment systems for hospitals. In most European health care systems, these payments replaced global budgets and per diem payments, whereas in the United States, the system replaced fee-for-service payments. As a result, the change in incentives and the objectives of the schemes differ. In the United States, the initial aim was to control total costs and discourage unnecessary treatments. In Europe, there has been greater emphasis on reducing unit costs and, in some countries, such as Norway and Sweden, reducing waiting lists through greater patient throughput.

Much of the literature is based on the US experience, but there is a growing literature on the experience of European health care systems. In this section, we review some of the evidence, highlighting contextual differences where appropriate.

Costs

Fixed-price payment systems incentivise providers to control costs and increase efficiency. Evidence of the impact on costs is mainly focused on unit costs, although there has been interest in the impact on total expenditure. This was of particular interest in the United States when DRG pricing was introduced into a system where the increasing total expenditure on health care was regarded as problematic (Sood et al 2008). However, the focus has generally been on improving efficiency through reductions in unit cost. Length of stay is known to be correlated with hospital charges (or price) (Polverejan et al 2003), and is commonly used as a measure of the inputs consumed (Chalkley and Malcomson 2000).

There is conflicting evidence about the impact that prospective payment had in the United States. Some early evidence suggested large decreases in the length of stay (for example, Kahn *et al* 1990), but Newhouse and Byrne (1988) and Carey (2000), using better-constructed analyses, found more modest reductions in the length of stay.

Casemix-based payments to hospitals are now widespread across Europe, and, despite the differing contexts into which DRGs have been applied, the findings are broadly similar. For example, Sweden was one of the earliest European adopters of DRG-based hospital financing during the late 1980s and 1990s (Kastberg and Siverbo 2007). County councils have implemented different hospital financing systems providing an opportunity to evaluate changes over time and between councils. Fosberg *et al* (2000), among others, observed an initial reduction in the length of stay in a number of councils adopting activity-based financing in the early 1990s. Charpentier and Samuelson (1996) found that these early productivity gains disappeared when examined over a longer period. Kastberg and Siverbo (2007) concluded that productivity gains were lost when the rules surrounding the new financing systems were relaxed over time.

In The Netherlands, prices are negotiated between private insurers and (mainly) public not-for-profit hospitals. Under this flexible price regime, the negotiations were dominated by price and volume. The Netherlands introduced a casemix-based payment system for around 20 per cent of acute hospital activity. As with PbR, one aim was to shift the emphasis in negotiations between insurer and provider away from price and towards quality improvements. Van de Ven and Schut (2009) reported that payments for activity funded according to DRGs was reduced by more than the price paid for other acute activity not covered by the fixed-price scheme.

The international literature generally supports the expectation that adoption of a prospective casemix-based payment for hospitals reduces unit costs as measured by length of stay, even if the effect is only temporary and perhaps small. Although there are exceptions, this evidence is drawn from a range of contexts. The experience of other countries suggests that the objective of encouraging efficiency is achievable, even in a system like the NHS in England that is characterised by public commissioners and providers and was previously funded by mainly prospective block grants.

Indeed, Farrar *et al* (2009) found strong evidence of reductions in unit costs after the introduction of PbR. They exploited the fact that PbR was introduced in phases in England and not at all in Scotland to conduct an analysis using data from England and Scotland for 2002–6. They used two measures of unit costs or patient-resource use: the proportion of patients treated as day cases; and the length of stay. Length of stay fell more quickly and the proportion of day cases increased more quickly where PbR was implemented. Similarly, an early study by Appleby *et al* (2005) using data from the first year after implementation of PbR (2003/4) attributed an increase in day-case activity to the introduction of the PbR tariff.

However, Mannion *et al* (2006) reported increased administrative costs associated with the new contracting process. Interviews with provider trusts and primary care trusts revealed an estimated increase in administrative costs per organisation of £100,000–180,000 and £90,000–190,000, respectively in 2006. Similarly, the Audit Commission (2005), drawing mainly on qualitative analysis from interviews plus some additional basic analysis of 2004/5 activity data, found that the costs of implementation were higher than expected (at around £100,000 per organisation), towards the lower end of the range reported by the respondents in the study by Mannion *et al* (2006).

Quality of care

Use of casemix-based payments may lead to skimping on the quality and intensity of treatment, which may later lead to readmission or higher mortality after discharge. International evidence is inconclusive on the effects on the quality of care of prospective-payment systems. One of the major challenges is securing the appropriate data to investigate changes in the quality of care. Many studies have used variables from administrative data as measures of quality, such as mortality in hospital and after discharge, and readmission rates after surgery or discharge, or surveys of patient satisfaction.

Again the literature is dominated by the US experience during the 1980s and 1990s. In a review of US research, Rosenberg and Browne (2001) found that the quality of care was not adversely affected by the introduction of prospective payment. Indeed, Kahn *et al* (1990) found that there was evidence to suggest that mortality fell after changes in the hospital-payment system for some types of care.

Other authors investigated patient stability at discharge using measures such as rate of discharge to long-term care (Sloan 1988), and clinical measures of stability (Kosecoff *et al* 1990). These studies found evidence that patients were discharged in a less stable condition under the prospective casemix-based funding.

Dismuke and Guimaraes (2002) examined the effect of a switch from retrospective to prospective casemix reimbursement in Portugal in the early 1990s. They found no change in inpatient mortality. However, their analysis was restricted to one DRG relating to common cerebrovascular disorders. In Sweden, changes have been assessed using health care professionals' perceptions of the quality of care (Charpentier and Samuelson 1996; Fosberg *et al* 2000). In the study by Fosberg and colleagues, doctors working in hospitals funded by prospective casemix considered that patients in their hospital were being discharged too quickly. However, comparisons of hard data on discharge patterns did not support this view.

Farrar *et al* (2009) investigated the impact of PbR on the quality of care in England. They used administrative data to construct standard indicators of the quality of hospital care: rates of in-hospital mortality, 30-day post surgical mortality, and emergency readmissions. The authors concluded that there had been no change in the quality of care as measured by the proxies used. However, it is possible that there may have been dimensions of quality of care that could have been adversely affected by PbR that were not captured in the study.

Activity

Nordic countries adopting activity-based financing have generally done so with the explicit aim of increasing productivity and reducing patient waiting times for hospital care (Siciliani and Hurst 2005). There is some empirical evidence of a positive relationship between DRG payment and output for Norway, although for Sweden the effects appear to have been temporary (Mikkola *et al* 2002; Kjerstad 2003).

Appleby *et al* (2005) examined whether there were increases in activity and associated reductions in waiting times in the first 15 HRGs subject to PbR in 2003/4. They hypothesised that because prices were based on average costs, low-cost providers would be more likely to respond to the incentive to increase activity. They found that while there were increases in admissions in some of the 15 HRGs, others experienced a fall, and there was no association between waiting times and the use of the tariff as provider costs did not appear to affect their response to the incentives. They identified a number of possible reasons for a lack of association: the small proportion of hospitals' income affected by the tariff at the time; the effects of waiting-time targets swamping the PbR effects; and the lack of information within trusts on their costs.

Mannion *et al* (2006) examined the use of demand-management methods following the introduction of PbR and patient choice in South Yorkshire. They noted a rise in acute elective and non-elective activity, although their methods did not allow them to attribute this to the introduction of PbR as they could not control for the effects of other factors.

The study by Farrar *et al* (2009) examining data up to 2005/6 found evidence of an increase in the volume of care, but this was sensitive to the control group used in the analysis. Using Scotland (where PbR was not implemented) as a control group, English hospitals experienced higher growth in spells of care, which appeared to be associated with the introduction of PbR. However, when using comparisons within the English system, the difference in growth between hospitals operating under tariff and those outside the tariff system disappeared. The authors concluded that other policies, such as waiting-time targets, may have been more important in driving the growth in the volume of care in England relative to that in Scotland.

Unintended effects

Gaming

One concern with prospective-payment systems is the potential for upcoding, where hospitals systematically categorise patients into HRGs that have a higher level of reimbursement.

Carter *et al* (1990) investigated upcoding following changes in Medicare payments in the United States. They used a private coding firm to recode a sample of medical charts between 1986 and 1987 and compare the hospital DRG assignment to recoded DRGs. They concluded that one-third of the change in casemix was attributable to upcoding, but this could be due to more accurate coding.

Dafny (2005) investigated the response by hospitals to a price change in 1988, when the age criterion that was attached to some DRGs was abolished, as a result of which the price-weighting of some DRGs increased. Following the policy change, there was an increase in upcoding, which was done in a sophisticated manner through the upcoding of DRGs that would give the greatest financial return.

Silverman and Skinner (2004) examined the US Medicare system over the period 1989–96, concentrating on respiratory-related DRGs by employing the chart-review method devised by Carter *et al* (1990). They found evidence that upcoding behaviour was related to hospital ownership (ie, for-profit or not-for-profit).

However, studies examining the impact of casemix-based payments in health care systems where the hospitals are predominantly publicly owned and the ability to retain surpluses is limited have found similar results. Serdén *et al* (2003) found that the introduction of case-based systems in Sweden led to a comparatively greater increase in the number of secondary diagnoses among hospitals paid under prospective-payment systems.

Aakvik and Kjerstad (2005) used Norwegian patient-level data from a group of hospitals paid by the prospective-payment system as well as from a control group of hospitals that were not. They looked at the percentage of complications, and compared the length of stay for patients between the two groups of hospitals. A small but significant increase in the percentage of complications was found in hospitals that had implemented prospective-payment systems. However, there was no significant difference in the length of stay between the two groups.

In general, the PbR tariff for HRGs 'with complication' receive a higher level of payment than those 'without complications', indicating a potential incentive to upcoding in England's NHS. Shortly after PbR was introduced, Rogers *et al* (2005) analysed activity data for evidence of upcoding. They found no evidence that there was a higher proportion of HRGs being coded 'with complications' at this early stage.

Yi *et al* (2007) examined the evidence of upcoding using data from English and Scottish hospitals, and compared coding of HRGs before and after the introduction of PbR in England. They found a higher rate of growth of spells in HRGs with complications in England compared with Scotland. However, the number of diagnoses in such HRGs decreased after PbR in comparison with the number of diagnoses in HRGs without complications. Furthermore, lengths of stay for HRGs with complications were shorter after the introduction of PbR, suggesting increased efficiency under PbR rather than unjustified upcoding. This work provides preliminary evidence of upcoding in the system.

Equity

So-called cream-skimming, or adverse selection, means selection by providers of patients who are expected to be (more) profitable, in this case in relation to the risk-adjusted payments based on average costs of treatment. When hospitals are able to decide the service mix (eg, foundation trusts), they could also choose to provide more of the profitable HRGs than the less profitable ones, and even get rid of specific specialties, which could be disadvantageous to specific local patient groups.

The risk of widening inequality in the use of services, given that PbR gave hospitals incentives to adjust their costs towards the national average, was examined by Cookson and Laudicella (2011). They studied whether hospital patients living in small areas of low socio-economic status cost more to treat than patients living in better-off areas to see if cream-skimming was to be expected. They looked at hip replacement as a tracer treatment, and used length of stay as an indication of cost. They showed that patients from the most deprived areas (the lowest 10 per cent of small areas on a standard measure of deprivation) stayed 6 per cent longer than those from the least deprived (the top 10 per cent of small areas) in 2001/2, but that this difference had fallen to 2 per cent by 2007/8. The major determinants of length of stay were age and number of diagnoses. Thus under the NHS fixed-price payment system, there were potential incentives for competing hospitals to cream-skim.

However, in a subsequent analysis, Cookson et al (2010b) found no obvious change in socio-economic equity of use from 2001/2 to 2008/9 for elective procedures, and some signs that equity might have improved slightly, since inpatient admission rates had risen slightly faster in low-income areas than elsewhere. This study found that socio-economic disparities in health care utilisation in the English NHS were relatively impervious to changes in the supply-side brought about by health care reforms affecting hospital reimbursement methods.

These conclusions reinforced similar findings from studies of health care equity in the 1990s, which found little or no change during a period of pro-competitive health reform coupled with much slower expenditure growth (Cookson et al 2010a). They concluded that as long as the NHS continued to provide universal and comprehensive care free at the point of delivery, policy-makers could safely embark on major programmes of efficiency-oriented reform without undermining socio-economic equity in health care.

Conclusion

There is only limited evidence available on the impact of PbR on the performance of the English NHS, and determining whether PbR has achieved its objectives is further complicated by the need to disentangle the effects of PbR from those of the other reforms introduced during the same period. Much has been written about the likely effects of the policy (Appleby and Renu 2004; Street and Sawson 2004; Street and Maynard 2007), but there has been only a limited amount of analysis based on empirical findings. The empirical studies have investigated a number of areas of impact: unit costs; quality of care; volume and waiting times; administrative costs; upcoding and cream-skimming.

The evidence broadly supports the conclusion that PbR (alongside the other New Labour reforms) was associated with reductions in unit costs as indicated by reductions in length of inpatient stay and increases in the proportion of patients treated as day cases. For such reductions to be interpreted as increases in efficiency, would require that quality remained unchanged or improved over the same period. Quality of care, as measured using patient-level administrative data, appeared not to have been adversely affected by the introduction of PbR. While there is no direct evidence that fixed prices led commissioners to focus on quality, the available evidence does at least suggest that providers focusing on cost reduction was not to the detriment of quality of care in the NHS in England. On the other hand, such analysis may not capture the wider impact on costs: while the transaction and administrative costs of operating PbR have not been fully documented, these are likely to have been quite large.

The fears that PbR would lead to widespread gaming and that certain (more expensive) patients would be dumped or deterred from accessing care have also proved to be ill-founded with respect to cream-skimming. The evidence to date on upcoding suggests that such fears may be justified.

Finally, although one objective of PbR was to encourage providers to increase activity, there is little evidence that it was the main reason for increased growth in activity during this period. Commissioners have had a tendency to blame PbR for rising hospital activity (*see* Chapter 8) and the expenditure associated with it, but in fact it would seem that other factors, such as waiting-time targets, might have been responsible.

In future, under the coalition government's proposals, the structure of tariff will be determined by the NHS Commissioning Board, and prices will be set by the new Monitor (*see* Chapter 10). Concerns have focused on the move away from fixed prices. The legislation allows future tariffs to be 'bundled', that is, to cover one or more specified services. There is a need to consider the applicability of HRGs to other sectors of the health system, and to seek alternative ways of defining pathways and packages of care, particularly ones that stretch beyond the confines of the hospital to include community and intermediate care services.

It is likely that the trend for setting prices at an efficient price or 'best-practice tariff' will continue rather than reverting to the basis of average costs. Prices also need better to reflect the true underlying costs (of both public and private providers), and the casemix adjustment needs to be sufficiently sophisticated to remove potential incentives for cream-skimming. If fixed prices and prospective-payment systems are to be extended to new specialties, this will require more patient-level costing data and more sophisticated methods for setting prices in future.

6 Competition between hospitals

Carol Propper and Jennifer Dixon

There has been an international trend over the past two decades to encourage more competition in health care by introducing market-related reforms, particularly in countries where health care is publicly financed and provided. Such reforms have included developing competition between providers; competition between insurers; the regulation of prices; greater information and choice for patients; and effective regulation of competition.

Those who promote competition in health care make an appeal to a simple economic argument: competitive pressure helps make private firms more efficient; firms cut costs and improve their goods and services in order to attract consumers, and this continual drive for improvement is good for the economy. Firms that are unable or unwilling to become more efficient will be priced out of the market, while new, more efficient, firms will enter the market. This logic is then transferred to the provision of health services. For example, giving health care purchasers or service users the ability to choose between providers applies competitive pressure to those providers and, analogous with private markets, they will raise their game to attract business.

At the same time, however, a number of studies have raised concerns about the functioning of markets in health care, particularly with regard to whether competition will deliver the socially optimal quality of care (Federal Trade Commission/US Department of Justice 2004). Quality is a major issue in health care because the effect of the quality of care on an individual's well-being can be very great.

England's National Health Service (NHS) has so far experienced two waves of policies to promote competition between suppliers of hospital care – the so-called internal market of the 1990s, and the Labour government's reforms of the 2000s – and, at the time of writing, the coalition administration is proposing to extend competition among the suppliers of services to the NHS in a further series of reforms. These will include:

- seeking to broaden the provider base

- placing the commissioning role with general practitioners (GPs) organised into GP commissioning consortia

■ using pro-competitive regulation rather than central-government direction to shape the resultant system.

The interesting issue of why market-type reforms have been so prevalent is not discussed here. This chapter has a more modest aim: to scrutinise the assumption that competition between hospital providers will lead to better care, focusing on the impact of competition on quality.

The next section begins with a review of the theoretical foundations for competition in health care. We then present a brief review of the findings from the United States, not because the US experience may be the most relevant, but simply because this is the country with the most empirical evidence on the impact of competition in health care. Next, we review the evidence from the United Kingdom, and we conclude by offering some reflections for policy-makers.

The impact of competition on health care markets: what economic theory predicts

Health care markets are thought to differ from textbook competitive markets in a number of important ways. These include the fact that:

■ the product is differentiated (due, for example, to a hospital's location or different styles of provision)

■ the information available to consumers is imperfect

■ government regulation is extensive as a result.

In addition, many organisations, even in a system like that of the United States, are not-for-profit (Dranove and Satterthwaite 2000), that is, they do not distribute profits to shareholders, but instead invest surpluses in the organisation. In these types of complex markets, standard economic theory fails to provide strong guidance about whether competition can provide beneficial results.

Theoretical models show that where there is product differentiation (as in the hospital market), competition can provide too little, too much, or just the right amount of quality or variety of services (Gaynor and Vogt 2000). The impact of competition will also depend on the responsiveness of the buyer of health care to both quality and price. This will depend on the extent to which price and quality can be measured and reported. If quality is measured accurately, but price is measured poorly, demand becomes less responsive to price, allowing providers to raise their prices. It can also give providers an incentive to increase – and possibly overproduce – quality. If price is measured accurately, but quality is measured poorly, then the levels of quality supplied will be too low. In addition, if quality has several attributes, some of which are easier to measure than others, competition may lead to overproduction of the easily measured attributes and underproduction of the others.

In markets where the buyers of health care are not very sensitive to price (for example, in a market where consumers have generous health insurance provided by employers that are not very cost-conscious) and there is no centralised price-setting (such as in the United States before the 1980s), buyers will be responsive to differences in quality. In such a market, price may be high, but quality will be correspondingly high. In markets where buyers have harder budget constraints (such as in the NHS during the internal market of the 1990s, discussed later in this chapter), price may be more important and hospitals will compete on prices, leaving quality to fall.

These predictions apply to markets where price is negotiated between the buyer and seller of health care. However, the price of health care is often fixed for all providers of a treatment by a regulator or government, as occurs under the diagnosis-related group (DRG) system used in the United States for Medicare by the federal government and by most private insurers as well (*see* Chapter 5). If prices are fixed in this way, there will be no competition on price, and competition will be based on quality. In this case, competition may lead to excessive levels of quality and excessive product differentiation (Gaynor 2004), but if the fixed price for a treatment is too low (below marginal cost), competition may lead to the quality of this treatment being too low.

In sum, the guidance that comes from the theoretical analyses for policy-makers is ambiguous. Further, the precise institutional structure of the market matters. Policy-makers therefore need to turn to the empirical evidence for guidance.

The US evidence on competition and health system outcomes

Almost all the evidence on the impact of competition between health care providers comes from the US market, and much of that from one – albeit very large – market, namely California. The results of these studies show that the impact of competition depends on the 'rules of the game': the institutional features of the health care market.

Three periods can be identified in the US health care market (Dranove and Satterthwaite 2000). In the first, during the 1960s and 1970s, consumers were covered by generous insurance and hospitals were reimbursed retrospectively for their full costs. In the second, beginning in the early 1980s, government payers (Medicare) introduced prospective-payment schemes and utilisation reviews (ie, the scrutiny of demands for treatment and thus expenditure with the option of refusing unjustified spending). Private insurers followed their lead. The third period – 'managed care' – began in the 1980s and took hold in the 1990s. This saw managed-care organisations enrol an individual for a set period for a fixed capitation payment. Managed-care organisations were thus concerned about price and very active in seeking information on quality.

Quality

In terms of the effect on quality, it is the generally accepted view (although empirical evidence is quite weak) that the first period resulted in a 'medical arms race' (Robinson and Luft 1985). As buyers were not sensitive to price, hospitals competed on quality, both to attract buyers and to attract physicians to practise at their hospitals. The impact of this raised both price and quality in areas with more hospitals (Joskow 1980).

More recent evidence has focused on the impact of competition under fixed prices. An influential early study focused on the treatment of elderly patients admitted to hospital with a heart attack and covered by government insurance (Medicare). Higher competition was associated with lower death rates from heart attack after 1990 (Kessler and McClellan 2000). Similar findings were reported by Rogowski *et al* (2007), who looked at deaths across a broader range of medical conditions, and Sari (2002) who measured the quality of health care by the number of in-hospital complications. However, other studies show either no effect on quality, or, in some cases, negative effects (Shortell and Hughes 1988; Ho and Hamilton 2000; Mukamel *et al* 2001; Gowrisankaran and Town 2003; Volpp *et al* 2003).

The incentives for hospitals to increase quality when operating in competitive markets may depend on the precise mix of payers that the hospitals have. There is evidence that capitated payers, such as health maintenance organisations (HMOs), prefer higher-quality hospital care (Schulman *et al* 1997; Chernew *et al* 1998; Escarce *et al* 1999; Gaskin *et al* 2002; Young *et al* 2002; Rainwater and Romano 2003). This leads to both price reductions and quality improvements in competitive environments where HMO-penetration is high (Mukamel *et al* 2001; Sari 2002; Rogowski *et al* 2007). Not all the evidence supports this view: Kessler and McClellan (2000) find no association between the two; and both Shortell and Hughes (1988) and Shen (2003) find higher HMO-penetration to be negatively associated with the quality of care offered by hospitals.

Efficiency

Over the past 20 years, the US market for hospital care has seen a substantial rise in hospital mergers (Gaynor and Haas-Wilson 1999) aimed at achieving cost reductions through economies of scale and decreased administrative costs, increasing market power relative to other providers (Harrison 2007), or increasing influence in negotiations for contracts with payers. A growing body of evidence demonstrates that hospital mergers lead to higher prices but few, if any, cost-savings (Noether 1988; Melnick *et al* 1992; Connor *et al* 1998; Dranove and Ludwick 1999; Keeler *et al* 1999; Dranove and Lindrooth 2003; Gaynor and Vogt 2003) or short-run improvements in efficiency and productivity (Ferrier and Valdmanis 2004).

Until recently, mergers between not-for-profit hospitals had been tolerated, as it was viewed that their not-for-profit status would mean that mergers would not have anti-competitive effects. Recent studies have challenged this view. Mergers by not-for-profits have been found to decrease competition and have an equally negative impact on outcomes as mergers by for-profits (Gaynor and Vogt 2003; Abraham *et al* 2007). The evidence on vertical mergers (for example, between primary- and secondary-care providers) is more complex (Haas-Wilson 2003).

Equity

Competition may also lead to differential treatment of different types of patients, although this outcome has been studied less. Kessler and Geppert (2005) examined the treatment given to elderly Medicare patients admitted to hospital following a heart attack. They investigated the extent to which competition had an impact on patients who were otherwise sicker, compared with those who were otherwise healthier. They found that in more competitive markets, there was greater variation in medical care. Furthermore, this variation was, on average, beneficial. Healthy patients in more competitive markets received less intensive treatment than those in more concentrated (less competitive) markets, without any significant difference in health outcomes. Sick patients in more competitive markets received more intensive treatment than similar patients in more concentrated (less competitive) markets, with the former having better health outcomes. The effect of competition appeared to be that there were more appropriate treatments – with greater variety in treatment styles – across hospitals in more competitive areas, and that neither patient group lost as a result.

Evidence from the NHS internal market in the 1990s

The internal market that operated in the NHS throughout the United Kingdom between 1991 and 1997 encouraged competition between NHS hospitals for contracts for hospital care from two sets of buyers: the geographically based district health authorities; and the smaller GP fundholders. Prices could be negotiated between hospitals and the buyers, and price lists (although not including any discounts) were supposed to be publicly available.

Information on quality was very limited, although there is weak evidence that greater competition was associated with lower costs (Söderlund *et al* 1997). Two large-scale studies of the association between hospital competition and quality suggest that quality – as measured by deaths of patients admitted to hospitals with heart attacks – actually fell during the internal market (Propper *et al* 2004, 2008a). This combination of falls in price and a drop in quality fits with the predictions of economic theory: where demanders are sensitive to price and quality information is weak, both prices and quality are likely to fall as competition increases.

In addition, there is a considerable body of evidence to suggest that the two types of purchasers were differentially able to reap the benefits from provider competition. GP fundholders were able to secure shorter waiting times for their patients, were more able to move contracts, and generally appeared to be more responsive to patients' wishes and more willing to exploit competition between hospitals for their patient referrals (Le Grand 1999; Croxson *et al* 2001; Propper *et al* 2002; Dusheiko *et al* 2004). This may have been partly due to their smaller size: district health authorities were concerned that if they removed their business, the local hospital risked failing. It was also likely to be due to self-selection among the GPs who became fundholders. Case-study evidence suggests that fundholders did not drop potentially expensive patients (known as dumping) (Matsaganis and Glennerster 1994), perhaps due to the presence of stop-loss insurance on expensive patients.

Evidence from New Labour's market reforms

The second phase of provider competition was represented by the market-based reforms reintroduced in England in the 2000s by the New Labour government. The combination of diversity of providers, patient choice and Payment by Results (PbR) (discussed elsewhere in this book) was designed to increase competition.

In theory, at least, NHS hospitals had incentives to respond to increased competition. Although NHS hospitals are public organisations, the regime they operated under gave hospital managers strong incentives not to make financial losses, although much weaker incentives to make surpluses. PbR increased uncertainty about income for hospitals, and the simultaneous rise in the availability of care from NHS and non-NHS competitors was also likely to have increased competition.

The economic literature (Gaynor 2004) suggests that an increase in the elasticity of demand, combined with a fixed-price regime, should lead to improvement in the quality of care in hospitals facing competition.

Two studies have sought to estimate the impact of the introduction of competition on both clinical and financial outcomes (Cooper *et al* 2011; Gaynor *et al* 2011). They used a very similar approach, with each looking at the behaviour of hospitals located in the markets that might be most affected by competition before and after the reintroduction of provider competition policy in the English NHS, and comparing this with the behaviour of hospitals located in markets where the policy was expected to have had less effect, using a 'difference-in-difference' research design. This approach controls for differences between urban and non-urban locations, for example, in the types of patient and hospital that are located in these different areas.

The argument underpinning both studies is that competition in hospital markets is geographically driven as, all other things being equal, patients prefer to be treated close to home. Hospitals in more dense (urban) markets therefore generally face greater competition, and so these hospitals will be exposed to more potential competition than those in rural areas. The strategy used in both studies was to compare the difference in outcomes before and after the policy change for hospitals located in areas where the market structure was such that competition was more likely than in areas with limited competition. The studies were therefore not based on a function of quality and measures of actual competition, as this could be hard to measure, but on the potential competitiveness of the market as measured by market structure.

In terms of the measurement of market structure, both studies based this on patient flows to NHS hospitals for elective care before implementation of the policy changes so as to pick up the pre-policy behaviour of patients and commissioners. For example, even if there is only one hospital in an area to which patients are prepared to travel, and/or buyers nevertheless place contracts with distant providers that they then force local patients to use, that hospital will still face more potential competition than one where buyers only place contracts with a single local hospital.

Both studies used elective flows to define the market structure because it was in elective care where the competition was expected to have an effect. Ideally, both studies would also have included independent-sector treatment centres (ISTCs) and private providers in these calculations, but a lack of data on patient flows made this impossible, and so market structure in both studies was defined in terms of NHS providers. In practice, this lack of private-sector data may make little difference as the role of the ISTCs was much smaller during the period than was initially expected.

Using patient flows, the two studies calculated a standard measure of market concentration, known as the Herfindahl-Hirschman Index (HHI), for each hospital. The higher the HHI, the closer the market structure was to a monopoly. The studies then examined the relationship between market structure pre-policy (as measured by the HHI), and measures of quality and other outcomes.

Impact on quality

Gaynor et al (2011) examined the effect of the reforms on hospital death rates after admissions for acute myocardial infarction (heart attack), and death rates after admission for any reason. Cooper et al (2011) examined only the effect on mortality rates for people admitted for heart attack. Gaynor et al used the period 2003–7 to cover before and after the reintroduction of competition; the Cooper study extended the 'after period' to 2008. Death rates were not employed because of competition for emergency patients, but rather because they are thought to be reliable markers of quality, particularly death rates for acute myocardial infarction, and they provide hospitals with the chance to improve quality by making various changes (Propper et al 2006).

Both studies concluded that death rates fell across the period for all hospitals, but they fell more for hospitals that were located in less concentrated (more potentially competitive) markets. This is shown in Figures 5 and 6, opposite, which plot the relationship between mortality and competition policy concentration (the extent to which competition is possible) before and after the reform. Each dot represents

Figure 5 Hospital mortality from acute myocardial infarction compared with
market structure pre- and post-reform

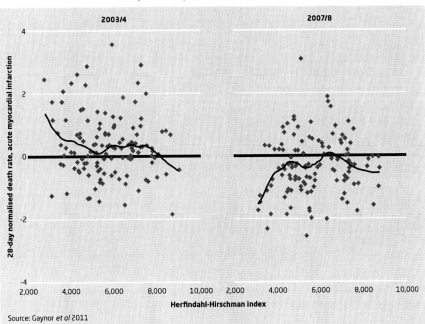

Source: Gaynor *et al* 2011

Figure 6 All-cause hospital mortality compared with market structure
pre- and post-reform

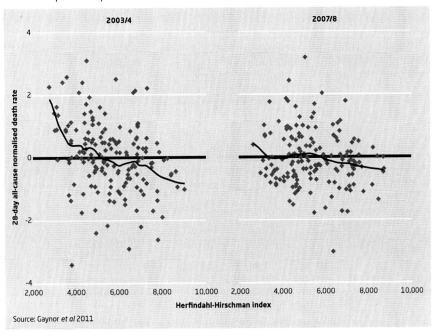

Source: Gaynor *et al* 2011

a hospital. Hospitals on the left hand side of each graph were in less concentrated markets before the policy was implemented – in other words they faced more potential competition once the policy came into force. Figure 5 (from Gaynor *et al* 2011) shows the relationship between the mortality rates of patients admitted following an acute myocardial infarction and market structure. The left hand panel shows that mortality was clearly higher in the less concentrated markets before the reform. But post-reform the direction of the association has been reversed, and mortality was lower in markets where more competition was possible.

The same pattern can be seen in Figure 6, which plots all-cause hospital mortality rates against market concentration. These plots show that quality increased more in hospitals that were more exposed to competition than those that were not. This is confirmed by statistical analysis in both studies.

Impact on efficiency

Gaynor *et al* (2011) also examined other clinical outcomes, including methicillin-resistant *Staphylococcus aureus* rates and length of stay, as well as simple measures of productivity and expenditure. They found that there were no differential effects of competition on these outcomes, except in the case of length of stay, which fell more in hospitals located in more competitive markets. Gaynor *et al* controlled for measurable differences in casemix using a range of indicators (although they acknowledged that there may still be selection on factors that cannot be measured).

The conclusions from both these studies is that patients discharged from hospitals located in markets where market concentration was lower – that is, markets in which the policy could have had a bigger effect – were less likely to die, had shorter length of stay, and were treated at the same cost.

Conclusions

The US evidence broadly suggests that inter-hospital competition has led to substantially lower prices since the 1990s. The impact on quality, however, is more mixed, with the general conclusion being that quality increases where prices are fixed, but may decline where they are not.

In England, the quantitative evidence on the impact on health outcomes of competition between hospitals in the health sector since 1997 rests on the two studies outlined above. Further research is needed to fully understand the implications of these findings for future policies on the role of competition and markets in health care as, inevitably in studies that rely on administrative data, both have limitations that affect their interpretability.

A number of other points must be borne in mind when reviewing the evidence.

- First, the English findings rely mainly on one measure of clinical quality – namely mortality rates. It will be important to assess the effect of competition on a wider set of process and outcome measures in future as data improve (eg, patient-reported outcomes related to the elective treatments for which competition is most relevant).

■ Second, as mentioned, the economics literature is weak with regard to exactly how competition between hospitals for elective patients might result in the staff within them (particularly the clinical staff) improving the quality of care in non-elective areas such as myocardial infarction. One interesting English study found that increasing competition among NHS hospitals was associated with better management practices within them (Bloom *et al* 2010), findings that replicate results found throughout private-sector businesses. This is one potential pathway; others need to be explored (*see* Chapter 9 for more on this).

■ Third, the impact of competition is heavily defined by the environment in which it is operating, eg, the features of the local market, the extent and types of regulation, the nature of price-setting and so on, and the interaction between these. While the studies reviewed above used techniques that tried to control for these and to identify the effect of competition, the fact that a range of more and less pro-competitive policies were introduced simultaneously means that more research is needed on precisely which aspects of reform led to change.

■ Fourth, the evidence reviewed in this chapter comes mostly from the United States. It is worth while speculating about what factors might be at work in that setting and how those may translate to England and the NHS. In the United States, price-sensitive insurers negotiate prices. These insurers have strong incentives to obtain lower prices, since their customers, typically employers, are responsive to price differences. Insurers, however, do not engage in sole-source contracting. They contract with sets or networks of hospitals. Patients are thus free to exercise choice of hospital within a network (which is often quite broad). As a result, hospitals have an incentive to compete on quality in order to attract patients within a network. There are both price and quality incentives in play that are very different from the situation in the English NHS market, in which many prices have been fixed and competition is between NHS trusts not between networks of hospitals.

Implications for future policy in the English NHS

The current coalition government is keen to increase the pace and scope of market-oriented reform in the English NHS (Department of Health 2010a). The research to date suggests that policy-makers should reflect on several issues in pursuing this agenda.

■ First, while the literature suggests that competition with regulated prices may bring benefits, the findings from settings where prices are deregulated are far more mixed, and for England in the 1990s were not encouraging. This suggests that any move to deregulate prices is at best premature. Even if quality information has improved, there is a danger that cash-constrained buyers operating within a tight fiscal environment will focus on cost-reductions at the expense of quality. Furthermore, in the NHS in England, many hospitals do not have adequate information about their costs to know if the price they are negotiating is above marginal cost.

■ Second, if purchasers themselves do not benefit from lower prices, their financial incentives will be weak and they will not drive price competition. The arrangements for GP commissioning consortia to keep surpluses are not yet spelled out in detail, although it is likely that they will be able to keep at least some. They will therefore have financial incentives to seek lower-cost providers, which is another reason to maintain fixed prices, at least until the behaviour of the consortia can be studied.

■ Third, competition for patients could also provide an incentive for GPs to be price-sensitive and, to the extent that patients can observe quality, be sensitive also to that in their choice of health care provider. The extent to which GP commissioning consortia will compete for patients is not yet clear. At present, competition for patients between GP practices is still limited.

■ Fourth, GP consortia may have an incentive to direct patients to lower-cost, as opposed to higher-quality, providers. GPs are often the ones providing advice and referring individual patients. In this context, it might be better to separate the functions of price negotiation from supporting patient choice and referral within the consortia in order to minimise the conflict between profits from lower prices and selecting the best-quality hospital (or other care) for patients.

■ Finally, competition between hospitals has been encouraged over the past decade largely in response to the need to reduce waiting times for elective treatments. The far greater challenge facing society and health care systems in future is caring for larger numbers of older people, the dying, and people with chronic conditions. The extent to which competition for elective care will have an impact on the quality of care for these people is not clear, and nor indeed is whether competition for chronic-care provision would work at hospital level. For this type of care and patient group, high-quality integrated care that promotes care closer to home is the objective, which is more likely to be achieved through vertical associations, or mergers, between primary care, social services and hospital care, which should reduce avoidable hospital costs (Commonwealth Fund Commission on a High Performance Health System 2006; Minott *et al* 2010). If competition, under the right conditions, is a means to extract better quality for the cost, it may be that the optimal unit of competition, at least for chronic and long-term care, is not a hospital, but a vertically integrated provider organisation.

7 Regulation and system management

Gwyn Bevan

As we have seen in previous chapters, the policies introduced into the English National Health Service (NHS) by the Labour government during the early 2000s were intended to develop provider competition on a level playing field and to enable patients to choose any willing provider in a market underpinned by regulation and system management.

These policies included innovations in:

- supply, eg, NHS foundation trusts and independent-sector treatment centres (ISTCs)

- commissioning, eg, world class commissioning and practice-based commissioning

- provider payment (Payment by Results)

- an emphasis on patient choice.

Each was covered by a research programme commissioned by the Department of Health to evaluate the main elements of the government's system reforms, although regulation was not included in this evaluation.

The relationship between regulation and the market-based health policies introduced is complex for two reasons.

First, the Labour government's proposals underwent several dramatic shifts (Stevens 2004; Robinson and Bevan 2005), as demonstrated in its three White Papers on system reform: *The New NHS* (Department of Health 1997), *The NHS Plan* (Department of Health 2000b), and *Delivering the NHS Plan* (Department of Health 2002a). The proposals in the first two White Papers explicitly sought quality improvement from public providers through regulation because provider competition was then deemed to be damaging or ineffective. Only in the third White Paper was it proposed to improve the quality of publicly funded health care through provider competition and patient choice.

Second, developments in the regulatory architecture lagged behind these shifts in policy. The principal role of the successive regulators of the quality of care – the Commission for Health Improvement (CHI), the Healthcare Commission and the Care Quality Commission (CQC) – was to improve quality through regulation.

In 2010, the coalition government redefined CQC's role as quality assurance for a market that is now assumed to be the principal driver of improved performance of publicly funded health care. The objective of quality assurance is therefore to ensure that the organisations providing publicly funded care are of adequate quality. In this light, what is most relevant for the future is evidence of past regulatory failure in the systems of quality assurance used by the CHI and the Healthcare Commission, where failure meant signalling that a provider's quality of care was adequate when it was not.

Drawing on published research that I have contributed to and also on my experience of working for the CHI, this chapter examines the regulation of public providers. First, we examine the shifts in government policies for publicly funded care. Next, we set out the tasks of the successive quality regulators along with those of the Audit Commission and Monitor. The next two sections discuss changes in the systems of assessment used by the CHI and the Healthcare Commission, and the evidence of their effectiveness. The chapter concludes by reflecting on that evidence, and considering its implications for the future design of effective regulation of quality of care in the NHS.

Changing regulatory policies: a third way

The mantra of *The New NHS* was 'what counts is what works' (Department of Health 1997, p 10), along with the idea that New Labour's policies offered a 'third way' (Giddens 1998) of running the NHS, namely by means of a system based on 'partnership and performance' rather than 'the old centralised command and control systems of the 1970s' or 'the divisive internal market system of the 1990s' (Department of Health 1997, p 10).

The government created two new regulators – the CHI and the National Institute for Clinical Excellence (NICE; renamed the National Institute for Health and Clinical Excellence in 2005).

The CHI was created in the wake of a series of scandals over quality of care (Abbasi 1998), particularly the Bristol case (Smith 1998), 'to support and oversee the quality of clinical services at local level, and to tackle shortcomings' (Department of Health 1997, para 3.7). The public inquiry into the management of the care of paediatric cardiac surgery patients at the Bristol Royal Infirmary found that there had been about 30 excess deaths there, along with systemic regulatory failure in that external bodies had been aware of the problem but had failed to take corrective action because of organisational confusion over responsibility for quality assurance (Kennedy 2001 p 2, pp 9–10, pp 186–203).

NICE was created 'to give a strong lead on clinical and cost-effectiveness, drawing up new guidelines and ensuring they reach all parts of the health service' (Secretary of State for Health 1997, para 3.5). One of NICE's functions was to decide what would and would not be available on the NHS in order to end so-called postcode rationing, the variation among health authorities in the availability of services such as *in vitro* fertilisation.

By 2000, the NHS was perceived to be in crisis, largely as a result of underfunding. The government's ensuing commitment to massive, unprecedented real growth in spending on the NHS resulted in a policy designed to change the traditional system of perverse incentives, described as follows.

> *The current system penalises success and rewards failure. A hospital which manages to treat all its patients within 9 or 12 months rather than 18 may be told that 'over performance' means it has been getting too much money and can manage with less next year. By contrast, hospitals with long waiting lists and times may be rewarded with extra money to bail them out – even though the root of the problem may be poor ways of working rather than lack of funding. The NHS has to move from a culture where it bails out failure to one where it rewards success.* (Department of Health 2000b, p 28)

The new policy was based on developing a regime of star-rating – a system of strong performance management from the centre plus public reporting of the performance of NHS organisations against national targets. Failing (zero-rated) organisations were 'named and shamed', and the jobs of their chief executives were at risk in the first two years (2001 and 2002). So-called three-star organisations were rewarded with what was known as 'earned autonomy', which later became a criterion for being eligible to become a foundation trust (Department of Health 2000b). Initially, the Department of Health was responsible for the star-ratings (Department of Health 2001a, 2002c), but the CHI took over in 2003 (Commission for Health Improvement 2003).

From 2002, the government introduced the policies of patient choice and competition among a plurality of providers (*see* Chapters 2, 4 and 6) alongside command and control by means of national targets and standards (Department of Health 2002a). As part of these policies, the Healthcare Commission was created in 2004, with the objective of creating a 'level playing field' with one regulator responsible for public and independent providers of health care. The two different regulators of quality of care – the CHI for the NHS and the National Care Standards Commission for independent providers of health and social care – were abolished. The Healthcare Commission continued to report on the performance of NHS organisations by publication of the star-ratings (Healthcare Commission 2004, 2005a) and, later, by means of the annual health check (Healthcare Commission 2006b, 2007b, 2008d).

In 2009, the Healthcare Commission was replaced by the CQC, which is responsible for regulating the quality of all providers of health and social care. The CQC produced the annual health check for 2009 (Care Quality Commission 2009), but, as part of the shift in emphasis from national targets to provider competition as the driver of improved performance, in 2010 the coalition government told it to cease carrying out the annual health check (West 2010). Independent providers continue to pay to be licensed, and, whereas regulation by the CHI and the Healthcare Commission of NHS providers was financed by the government, these providers must now also pay a fee to be registered by the CQC.

Five regulatory bodies

The Labour government was notable for creating and then abolishing a number of bodies with regulatory responsibilities for health care (Walshe 2003), and this turbulence has continued with the coalition government. This section outlines the functions of the three successive regulators of quality in the NHS – the CHI, the Healthcare Commission and the CQC – and the two organisations with which they had or have joint responsibilities. The focus is on their responsibilities for England. Some of the CHI's functions originally covered Wales, but the Healthcare Commission and the CQC cover England only. Following devolution in 1999, policies in the two countries increasingly diverged (Greer 2004; Connolly *et al* 2010).

The CHI

The CHI was created in 2000 and abolished in 2004. Box 5, opposite, outlines its initial functions and shows how these were expanded in 2003. As the regulator of the quality of care of NHS providers, the CHI's principal task was to undertake and report on clinical governance reviews (CGRs), which assessed how well NHS providers were implementing the systems and processes of clinical governance (Scally and Donaldson 1998) (*see* below) and the NICE guidelines.

The CHI also undertook:

- investigations of serious or persistent problems of quality caused by systemic failures (Department of Health 1998)

- studies of the implementation of national service frameworks (NSFs), undertaken jointly with the Audit Commission

- and star-ratings (in 2003 only).

The Healthcare Commission

The Healthcare Commission took over from the CHI in 2004, and was abolished in 2009. The Healthcare Commission continued the programme of CGRs, studies of the implementation of NSFs (jointly with the Audit Commission), and publication of star-ratings until 2006, when the Healthcare Commission implemented its own systems for regulating the NHS based on the annual health check (Box 6, opposite).

Box 5 The regulatory functions of the CHI

From April 2000, the CHI was responsible for:

- undertaking and reporting on CGRs for NHS trusts and primary care trust providers

- developing and disseminating clinical governance principles and best practice throughout the NHS

- studying the implementation of NSFs and NICE guidelines

- investigating serious or persistent problems of quality caused by systemic failures.

From April 2003, the CHI was additionally responsible for:

- contracting for annual national surveys of staff and patients

- contracting for national clinical audits

- publishing star-ratings

- publishing an annual report to parliament on national progress on health care.

Sources: Department of Health 1998, pp 51–62; Department of Health 2002c, pp 64–66

Box 6 The regulatory functions of the Healthcare Commission

The Healthcare Commission was responsible for:

- reviewing the performance of each NHS organisation and awarding an annual rating

- regulating health care provided by the independent sector

- investigating serious service failures in the NHS

- carrying out reviews of the provision of health care in the NHS (including reviews of the economy and efficiency of the provision of health care)

- considering complaints about NHS bodies that had not been resolved locally

- reporting annually to parliament on the state of health care in England and Wales

- promoting the effective co-ordination of reviews or assessments of the provision of health care.

Source: Healthcare Commission 2009b, pp 7–8

In addition, the Healthcare Commission had responsibility for:

- licensing independent providers of health care

- undertaking studies of value for money in the NHS (with a transfer of this responsibility and staff from the Audit Commission).

The CQC

The CQC took over the regulation of health care from the Healthcare Commission in 2009, and was given additional responsibilities for:

- regulating adult social care

- monitoring functions by the Mental Health Act Commission on the operation of the Mental Health Act 1983

- registering general medical practices, doctors who work solely within private practice, and all primary dental care providers (whether NHS or private).

The review of arm's-length bodies (Department of Health 2010e) proposed only limited changes to the CQC, the main ones being to transfer responsibility for assessing NHS commissioners from the CQC to the NHS Commissioning Board, and to create HealthWatch England as a new, independent, consumer champion with a distinct identity within the CQC.

Box 7, below, gives CQC's regulatory functions before these proposed changes.

Box 7 The regulatory functions of the CQC

The CQC was to monitor:

- the medical and clinical treatment given to people of all ages, including treatment in hospitals and by the ambulance service and mental health services (eventually to include primary care such as GP and dental practices)

- the care provided in residential homes, in the community, in adult patients' own homes, and in residential care homes for children

- the services provided for people whose rights are restricted under the Mental Health Act

- the care provided by both the NHS and the independent sector.

Source: Care Quality Commission 2011

The Audit Commission

The Audit Commission was created in 1983 with a focus on local government. Its remit was extended in 1991 to encompass auditing the financial accounts of NHS bodies, and undertaking studies of value for money (Campbell-Smith 2008).

When in opposition, the Labour Party had considered giving the responsibilities of the CHI to the Audit Commission (Day and Klein 2001, p 98), but once in government it decided against this because the Audit Commission enjoyed such independence that it was able set its own priorities.

The Audit Commission undertook studies of NSFs jointly with the CHI and the Healthcare Commission, and, also jointly with the Healthcare Commission, evaluated the government's market-based reforms (Audit Commission and Healthcare Commission 2008). The annual health check assessments of the use of resources by NHS trusts (other than foundation trusts) were conducted by the Audit Commission.

On 13 August 2010, the coalition government announced that the Audit Commission would be abolished by 2012.

Monitor

Monitor was created in 2004 to regulate foundation trusts (*see* Box 8 below). It relied on the Healthcare Commission, and in future will rely on the CQC, for information

---

Box 8 The regulatory functions of Monitor

Monitor was created to:

- determine whether NHS trusts were ready to become NHS foundation trusts based on the criteria of good governance, financial viability, and being legally constituted, with a membership that was representative of their local community

- assess the governance of NHS foundation trusts, ensuring that they had complied with the conditions they had agreed to, namely that they:
  - were well-led and financially robust enough to operate effectively, efficiently and economically
  - met health care targets and national standards
  - co-operated with other NHS organisations

- support NHS foundation trust development.

Source: Monitor 2011

---

on the quality of care. The annual health check assessments of the use of resources by foundation trusts were conducted by Monitor.

The review of arm's-length bodies (Department of Health 2010e) proposed that Monitor be transformed into a new economic regulator for the NHS.

Changes in assessment systems

Box 9, below, outlines the seven pillars of clinical governance (as adopted after some development), and Figure 7, opposite, shows how the CHI's CGRs were designed to assess these systems and processes. The government specified key elements in CGRs (Department of Health 1998), but the process was designed by the CHI (Bevan and Cornwell 2006) and influenced by the Baldrige awards for quality in the United States (*see* Baldrige 2011).

The process of CHI's CGRs developed over time, and Box 10, opposite, outlines its final form, including the requirement for trusts to respond by producing an action plan (Bevan and Cornwell 2006). The CHI developed a scoring system for the seven pillars:

I – little or no progress

II – implementation in part

III – substantial progress

IV – excellent.

Box 9 The seven pillars of clinical governance

Processes for quality improvement

- Consultation and patient involvement
- Clinical risk management
- Clinical audit
- Research and effectiveness

Staff focus

- Staffing and staff management
- Education, training and continuing personal and professional development

Use of information

- Use of information to support clinical governance and health care delivery.

Source: Commission for Health Improvement 2002c, pp xii–xiii

Figure 7 The CHI's model for clinical governance

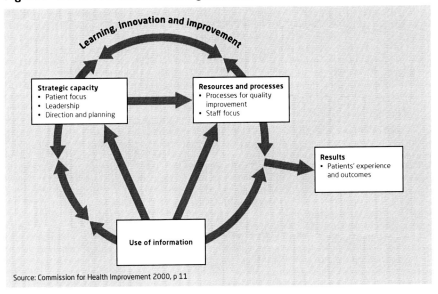

Source: Commission for Health Improvement 2000, p 11

Box 10 The process of CGRs

■ CGRs were based on a rolling programme of visits to every NHS trust responsible for delivering services, mainly selected at random.

■ Inspections were by multidisciplinary teams led by the review manager (a staff member of the CHI) and included a nurse, a doctor, an NHS manager, a lay member and another clinical professional (not a doctor or a nurse) recruited through national advertising, carefully selected and trained.

■ Before each visit (which lasted a week), data from national datasets, the trust and stakeholders (including patients and carers) were collected and analysed. The purpose of the visit was to interview staff, observe practice, verify information already obtained and gather further information.

■ The CHI's reports, drafted by the CHI's review managers and published both in hard copy and on the CHI's website, sought to:
  – identify areas for improvement
  – provide a way of identifying and acknowledging success and good practice, and encouraging its dissemination
  – take account of comments by the trust on factual accuracy.

■ The trust was required to develop an action plan in response to the key areas for action outlined in the report.

Source: Bevan and Cornwell 2006

The model used by the CHI for star-ratings of NHS acute trusts in England for 2003 employed three different sets of indicators – key targets, CGR scores, and indicators in three domains in a balanced scorecard – to produce a single summary score (*see* Box 11 below).

Box 11 The CHI's model of star-ratings of NHS acute trusts for 2003

- There were nine key targets, of which six were waiting times with the other three being measures of financial balance, hospital cleanliness, and improving the working lives of staff.

- CGRs were scored against the seven pillars of clinical governance.

- A wider set of about 40 targets and indicators, called the balanced scorecard, was organised into three domains: clinical outcomes, patient experience, and organisational capability and capacity.

Source: Commission for Health Improvement 2011

As CGRs were organised on a four-year rolling programme, the scores in CGR reports became out of date. CHI revised these scores based on reports from strategic health authorities on the progress that trusts had made in implementing their action plans. In outline, a trust with a current CGR:

- was at risk of being zero-rated for failures against more than one key target

- or for failure to make progress (I) in five or more of the pillars of clinical governance

- and was given three stars for good performance against key targets and the balanced scorecard, and reasonable performance in clinical governance (Bevan and Cornwell 2006).

For 2004 and 2005, the Healthcare Commission based star-ratings on key targets and the balanced scorecard only. From 2006, the annual health check was the primary basis of the Healthcare Commission's regulation of the quality of NHS providers, and was based on targets (similar to those of star-ratings) and so-called core and developmental standards.

Table 4, below, details the intended outcomes of the core and developmental standards: core standards were 'the minimum level of service patients and service users have a right to expect'; and developmental standards signalled the direction of travel for further improvement (Department of Health 2004c, p 3).

Table 4 Core and developmental standards for the annual health check for 2006/7

Standards	Intended outcome
Safety	Patient safety is enhanced by the use of health care processes, working practices and systemic activities that prevent or reduce the risk of harm to patients
Clinical and cost-effectiveness	Patients achieve health care benefits that meet their individual needs through health care decisions and services based on what assessed research evidence has shown provides effective clinical outcomes
Governance	Managerial and clinical leadership and accountability, as well as the organisation's culture, systems and working practices ensure that probity, quality assurance, quality improvement and patient safety are central components of all the activities of the health care organisation
Patient focus	Health care is provided in partnership with patients, their carers and relatives; it respects their diverse needs, preferences and choices, and is co-ordinated with other organisations (especially social care) whose services impact on patient well-being
Accessible and responsive care	Patients receive services as promptly as possible, have choice in access to services and treatments, and do not experience unnecessary delay at any stage of service delivery or along the care pathway
Care environment and amenities	Care is provided in environments that promote patient and staff well-being and respect for patients' needs and preferences in that they are designed for the effective and safe delivery of treatment, care or a specific function, provide as much privacy as possible, are well maintained and are cleaned to optimise health outcomes for patients
Public health	Programmes and services are designed and delivered in collaboration with all relevant communities to promote, protect and improve the health of the population served and reduce health inequalities between different population groups and areas

Source: Healthcare Commission 2006c, pp 32–6

Box 12, below, shows the Healthcare Commission's model for the assessment of core standards, which was largely based on self-assurance (*see* below).

The key elements and essential standards for quality and safety of care in the CQC's new system of registration of NHS providers are outlined in Box 13, opposite.

Box 12 The Healthcare Commission's model for assessing core standards for the annual health check

- A formal declaration by the board of every NHS trust of the extent to which, in its view, it had complied with the core standards.

- A commentary by third parties (from groups representing patients and the public and the oversight and scrutiny committees of local government) to be included in the trust's self-declaration and made public at the time of submission.

- An analysis by the Healthcare Commission of the data submitted by trusts in their self-declarations.

- A visit (inspection) on the basis of risk, as identified by the trust or the Healthcare Commission, or (for percentage) on a random basis.

- A qualification of the trust's declaration where there is significant discrepancy between what the trust declared and what the commission's evidence or visits demonstrated.

- A rating of performance for each trust.

Source: Healthcare Commission 2009b, pp 13–14

Box 13 Elements in the CQC's approach to ensuring that NHS providers have complied with the standards of quality and safety of care

Element	Outline
Quality and risk profile	A tool that gathers all the information CQC know about a provider to assess risk and prompt regulatory activity.
Essential standards of quality and safety of care	These are: ■ respecting and involving people who use services; consent to care and treatment ■ care and welfare of people who use services ■ meeting nutritional needs ■ co-operating with other providers ■ safeguarding vulnerable people who use services; cleanliness and infection control ■ management of medicines ■ safety and suitability of premises ■ safety, availability and suitability of equipment; requirements relating to workers ■ staffing ■ supporting workers ■ assessing and monitoring the quality of service provision; complaints; records.
Judgement framework	Provides a framework for assessors when making a judgement about compliance, as well as a guide for providers about the judgements CQC will make.
Setting the bar	Guidance for inspectors and assessors on what regulatory response they should take when concerns are identified.
Review of compliance report	Summarises the findings of a review of compliance including any improvement actions or enforcement activity for publication.
Provider compliance assessment	Tool for providers to evidence their compliance with essential standards.
Outcome evidence	The evidence used to demonstrate the outcomes described in the Guidance about compliance.
Site visit	To gather additional information an assessor may visit a site to carry out observations, interviews and discussions.

Evaluations of the Commission for Health Improvement and the Healthcare Commission

This section considers four issues in the evaluation of the CHI's CGRs and the Healthcare Commission's annual health check:

- their objectives
- proportionality
- consistency
- effectiveness in quality improvement and quality assurance.

Objectives

The CHI and the Healthcare Commission had two objectives in regulating the quality of NHS providers:

- quality improvement for all providers
- quality assurance by means of identifying, to ministers and the public, the providers with which there appeared to be problems.

This was difficult as the government required both regulators to use one principal instrument for both objectives (the CHI used CGRs, and the Healthcare Commission the annual health check). There was a crucial shift in what each regulator was required to report:

- the CHI's CGRs reported on the implementation of the *systems and processes of clinical governance* by NHS trusts
- the Healthcare Commission's annual health check reported on the *quality of services directly* (as 'excellent', 'good', 'fair' or 'weak').

Walshe (1999, p 194) presciently asked troubling questions about the CHI's CGRs: would these reports on the systems and processes of clinical governance satisfy the public and politicians, or would they want to know about actual quality of care? Reports on clinical governance would be easier to produce reliably and have the potential to improve quality, but would it be possible for a regulator to report reliably on quality in large and complex acute trusts?

These questions can now be answered with the benefit of hindsight, and pose a serious regulatory dilemma. The public and politicians do prefer the regulator to report directly on the quality of care (as in the annual health check) rather than on systems and processes (as in CGRs), but it is much more difficult to do the former than the latter.

Proportionality

Proportionality entails optimising the costs and benefits of regulation. Walshe (1999) asserted that the CHI's CGRs based on visiting every NHS provider organisation were not targeted and proportionate.

There are two reasons why this assertion was misdirected. First, the CHI's remit was not the single objective of quality assurance, but also to promote good practice, and so the CGRs sought to identify examples of both good and bad practice. Second, with regard to the objective of quality assurance, the CHI's experience was that, for typical acute trusts, the regulatory question was 'not which *organizations* to target, but which *parts of each organization* to target' (Bevan and Cornwell 2006, p 18).

Later, Benson *et al* (2004) rightly criticised the CHI's approach as not being proportionate because it used the same level of resources for each review and did not take account of the scale of organisations.

The CHI's CGRs did impose a regulatory burden on NHS trusts, but the review of inspection and monitoring in health care undertaken jointly by the Cabinet Office's Regulatory Impact Unit Public Sector Team and the Department of Health (Cabinet Office/Department of Health 2003) did not recommended any radical changes, and neither did the evaluation of clinical governance by the National Audit Office (2003).

The Healthcare Commission's regulatory approach aimed to reduce the regulatory burden by being proportionate for both quality assurance and improvement. This approach was based on using a system of self-assurance backed by external scrutiny from local organisations and checks from inspections of 20 per cent of trusts, half of which were chosen at random and half based on their estimated risk. The Office for Public Management's survey of NHS trusts found that they had concerns about gaming (by other trusts) when reporting was based on self-assurance, and that 'those selected at random generally understood why they had been selected but the risk based sample generally did not' (Office for Public Management 2008, p 33).

Consistency

Consistency is tied to the use of explicit standards. There is, however, a trade-off between consistency and effectiveness: limiting regulation to explicit standards is more likely to be consistent, but organisations may respond by focusing on satisfying those standards at the cost of neglecting other processes, which can result in poor quality of care (Bevan and Cornwell 2006).

The CHI was not empowered to specify standards, was unable to wait for the government to do so (Bevan and Cornwell 2006) and, largely as a consequence, its CGRs were criticised for lacking consistency (Benson *et al* 2004; Day and Klein 2004). The Healthcare Commission did use standards for the annual health check, but Shaw (2004) criticised them for not offering a sound basis for regulation because they varied in depth, scope and specificity.

Trusts experienced problems with interpreting what 'compliance' with standards meant and hence there were questions over the consistency with which these would have been reported by different organisations (Scrivens 2007). There were also problems over consistency in the checks on these reports from inspections (Scrivens 2007; Office for Public Management 2008, p 35).

Effectiveness

Ayres and Braithwaite (1992) argued that an effective regulator ought to 'speak softly but carry a big stick' at the top of a hierarchy of sanctions to ensure that the failings identified by the regulator are corrected. Webster (2002) questioned whether the CHI could be effective as its powers were initially limited to reporting (like the previously ineffectual Hospital Advisory Service, later the Health Advisory Service).

Like the Healthcare Commission, the CHI could only recommend that the Secretary of State impose special measures, which 'might include recommendations for practical assistance or organisational support from outside the trust or, in extreme circumstances, suspension of a service' (Healthcare Commission 2008b, p 23). The Healthcare Commission made three such recommendations, which were accepted by the secretary of state.

The CHI was not empowered to set deadlines for trusts to produce action plans in response to CGRs, and the key responsibility for putting pressure on trusts to do so lay with regional bodies, which were being reorganised. The CHI did, however, carry 'a big stick' when its CGRs fed into star-ratings, as lack of progress in the seven pillars of clinical governance could result in a zero-rating, or denial of three stars, along with the sanctions associated with those outcomes (Bevan and Cornwell 2006).

In assessing the effectiveness of both the CHI and the Healthcare Commission as independent regulators, it is vital to recognise that this is also an assessment of the way the government designed their regulatory instruments and powers. This section first considers the evidence for quality improvement, which comes from a positive impact of regulation. It then considers the evidence for quality assurance, which is negative, and of regulatory failure: did the regulator signal to ministers and the public that a provider's care was adequate when it was poor?

Quality improvement

Three instruments of quality improvement were used by the CHI and the Healthcare Commission:

- CGRs
- star-ratings
- the annual health check.

CGRs

The National Audit Office (2003) found that more than 90 per cent of members and senior managers of trusts reported that they had taken action in response to the CHI's CGRs, and that this had had the biggest impact on them of the various national initiatives (including star-ratings).

Benson *et al* (2004, pp 29–37) also found that the great majority of CHI's recommendations had resulted in action, with much of this attributed to CHI's intervention.

Star-ratings

The period between 2000 and 2005 offered the basis for evaluation of a so-called natural experiment between the NHS in England and that in the devolved countries in the United Kingdom (Scotland, Wales and Northern Ireland). Over this period:

- each country's NHS experienced sustained and unprecedented increases in funding (with England having the lowest per capita spending throughout)

- the governments in each country had common policy objectives, with targets to reduce hospital waiting times and improve the speed of responses by ambulances to life-threatening emergency calls

- no country had a system of provider competition in place

- only in England was there a regime of performance management and public reporting that applied sanctions for failure to hit targets and rewards for success; in Scotland and Wales there was the perception that failure was still capable of being rewarded (Bevan 2010).

Evaluations of this natural experiment found that the star-ratings regime resulted in a transformation in the reported performance of the NHS in England – particularly in bringing down waiting times for hospitals (Auditor General for Wales 2005; Bevan and Hood 2006a; Hauck and Street 2007; Propper *et al* 2008b; Besley *et al* 2009; Bevan 2009, 2010; Connolly *et al* 2010; Propper *et al* 2010a) and ambulance response times to potentially life-threatening emergencies (Auditor General for Wales 2006; Bevan and Hamblin 2009) – but not in the other three UK countries. Although the systems of regulation were not designed to counter gaming (Bevan and Hood 2006b), this appears to have been limited (Bevan and Hamblin 2009; Connolly *et al* 2010; Propper *et al* 2010a).

Examinations of the scoring system of star-ratings raised questions about the selection and aggregation of indicators into a single score (Commission for Health Improvement 2004a; Jacobs and Smith 2004; Bevan 2006; Jacobs *et al* 2006) and the transparency of the scoring system (Spiegelhalter 2005). Qualitative research has shown that when a trust was zero-rated, it had a devastating effect on staff morale (Mannion *et al* 2005).

The annual health check

The survey by the Office for Public Management (2008) of NHS trusts with regard to the three components of the annual health check for 2006/7 found that 90 per cent thought that targets and the core standards had been effective in driving improvement (p 22), fewer than 50 per cent thought that the developmental standards were effective (p 23), and there was criticism of targets: 'We work in pathways but the system measures us in bits' (p 23). More than 90 per cent saw self-assessment and inspections as triggers for change (p 40).

The Healthcare Commission's summary of external evaluations reported improvements over time in the self-assessments of the quality of services of NHS trusts from 2005/6 to 2006/7, but identified problems with primary care trusts following their reorganisation. They were 'the poorest performing sector and the only sector for which performance *deteriorated* as a whole' in 2006/7 (Healthcare Commission 2008c, p 36, original emphasis).

Quality assurance

There were two principal instruments of quality assurance: the CHI's CGRs, over which there were no public concerns; and the Healthcare Commission's annual health check, about which the House of Commons Health Committee observed: 'Doubts about the effectiveness of regulation have been raised by the fact that none of the recent appalling cases of lethally unsafe care in the NHS was brought to light by the annual health check' (House of Commons Health Committee 2009, p 75). These 'cases of appalling care' included 'Stoke Mandeville Hospital, and Maidstone & Tunbridge Wells NHS Trust, which involved stark failures in preventing and controlling healthcare-associated infections, and Mid-Staffordshire Trust, where wholly inadequate Accident and Emergency (A&E) care led to unnecessary deaths and harm' (p 10).

Table 5, opposite, gives the scores for each of the seven pillars of clinical governance for these three trusts following their CGRs in 2002. None did well on any pillar, and each had made no progress on two or more.

The problems of regulatory failure

The CHI's CGR of Stoke Mandeville Hospital for 2002 identified improving the control of infection as a key area for action. In 2004 and 2005, 'over 30 people died there as a consequence of two outbreaks of infection caused by the bacterium *Clostridium difficile*' (Healthcare Commission 2006a, p 2). This occurred before the annual health check, when the only current public information on quality of care was from star-ratings, which gave Buckinghamshire Hospitals NHS Trust (responsible for Stoke Mandeville) two stars (with a low score on the indicators of quality of care in the balanced scorecard) (Healthcare Commission 2005a, p 31).

In his foreword to the Healthcare Commission's investigation into the outbreaks of *Clostridium difficile* infection there, chairman Professor Sir Ian Kennedy

Table 5 Scores for the seven pillars of clinical governance for three NHS trusts in 2002

Pillars of clinical governance	Mid Staffordshire General Hospitals NHS Trust	Stoke Mandeville Hospital	Maidstone & Tunbridge Wells NHS Trust
Clinical audit	II	I	II
Clinical risk management	II	II	I
Continuing personal and professional development	II	II	II
Education and training	II	II	II
Research and effectiveness	II	I	I
Staffing and staff management	I	I	II
Use of information to support clinical governance and health care delivery	I	I	I

Source: Commission for Health Improvement 2002a, 2002b, 2002c

noted: 'what happened at Stoke Mandeville reflects many of the organisational failings identified in the Bristol report'. He went on to acknowledge regulatory failure from reporting after the event, but intended to correct this by developing the Healthcare Commission's 'capacity to identify when things are going wrong, before they end in tragedy... by using our techniques of surveillance, examining data on the performance of organisations providing healthcare on a regular basis, and by working with others' (Healthcare Commission 2006a, p 2).

The CHI's CGR of Maidstone & Tunbridge Wells NHS Trust for 2002 also identified improving the control of infection as a key area for action. There were serious outbreaks of *Clostridium difficile* there in the autumn of 2005 and in early 2006, but the Healthcare Commission's new system failed to detect it: the annual health check for 2005/6 reported that the trust was compliant with the core national standard for control of infection (Bevan 2008).

The CHI's CGR of Mid Staffordshire (which is used here to encompass Mid Staffordshire NHS Foundation Trust and its former status as Mid Staffordshire General Hospitals NHS Trust) for 2003 highlighted problems with:

- staff shortages among senior nurses, doctors and middle management

- poor quality of clinical data

- weaknesses in handling informal complaints and involving patients

- and the trust giving more attention to improving its financial position and performance on waiting times at the expense of a focus on quality of patient care (Commission for Health Improvement 2003).

The trust was rated on quality of services in successive annual health checks as:

- 'fair' in 2005/6 and 2006/7

- as one of the four '*most improved* acute and specialist trusts' in 2006/7 (Healthcare Commission 2007b, p 33, emphasis added)

- and provisionally as 'good' in 2007/8 (Healthcare Commission 2008d, p 93).

The Healthcare Commission's investigation into Mid Staffordshire identified all the problems that the CHI had highlighted six years previously, but exacerbated by pressure on the trust in 2006/7 'to stabilise its finances, and become an NHS foundation trust', requiring it to save £10 million (Healthcare Commission 2009a, p 9).

The report of the investigation was criticised by Bird (2009) for its inadequate documentation of mortality statistics. One of these inadequacies was the omission of an estimate of the number of excess deaths at the hospital, which was widely reported in the media as 400 (compared with 30 excess deaths at Bristol in the 1990s).

The problems at Mid Staffordshire were so grave that subsequently there have been official reports by Colin Thomé (2009) and Alberti (2009), an independent inquiry (Francis 2010), and a public inquiry (still in progress at the time of writing). The published reports depict an organisation failing in clinical governance with shocking accounts of indignity and suffering inflicted on patients. What also emerges is that there was such organisational turmoil and confusion that, as at Bristol in the 1990s, there was no effective system for assuring and monitoring the quality of care at Mid Staffordshire.

The reason the Healthcare Commission classified Mid Staffordshire's quality of services as 'good' in the annual health check assessment for 2007/8 was that it was then under investigation (Healthcare Commission 2008d, p 93) because the Healthcare Commission did not accept the trust's explanation that its high standardised mortality ratios were an artefact of coding. Monitor, however, did accept that explanation, and therefore granted the trust foundation trust status. The House of Commons Health Committee reported that 'the two organisations were not in communication about the Trust, and the [Healthcare Commission] only found out by accident that Monitor had decided to grant it Foundation Trust status' (House of Commons Health Committee 2009, para 244, p 79).

None of the external organisations that the Healthcare Commission relied on for checks on the trust's reports for the annual health check based on its self-assurance – the primary care trust, the strategic health authority, or local oversight and scrutiny committees – detected anything wrong with the trust's performance until after the Healthcare Commission investigation (Colin Thomé 2009). Colin Thomé points out that Monitor looked to the primary care trusts and strategic health authorities to raise concerns about the trust's quality of care when it applied for foundation status, but that these organisations 'assumed that regulation of quality would be fulfilled by the Healthcare Commission and Monitor' (Colin Thomé 2009, p 22).

Lessons for the future of regulation

This chapter concludes by seeking to draw lessons from the past to inform the future, drawing on the review of the three regulatory instruments used by the CHI and the Healthcare Commission: star-ratings, CGRs and the annual health check.

There is strong evidence from the evaluations of the star-rating regime that this had a direct and powerful effect in improving the reported performance of the English NHS in terms of shorter hospital waiting times and ambulance response times, both over time, and as compared with the performance of the NHS in the other three countries of the United Kingdom. With apologies to Winston Churchill (who was commenting on democracy), New Labour's target regime was described by Bevan (2009) as 'the worst system ever invented except for all the others', and needed development to take account of local circumstances, which the CHI would have sought to do if it had not been abolished.

The evidence on quality improvement from CGRs and the annual health check is less strong than that for star-ratings. Both have been assessed by means of surveys of those who were subjected to CGRs and the annual health check. The impact of the annual health check has also been assessed in terms of the improvement in scores based on self-assurance.

Patient choice and competition are seen as the policy instruments that will drive future improvements. With that in mind, what can be learned from the CHI's CGRs and the Healthcare Commission's annual health check that might enhance the CQC's role in quality assurance and ensure that the public can have confidence in the quality of care provided by registered and licensed suppliers?

The main feature of the CHI's CGRs was a rolling programme of visits to all NHS trusts by teams that undertook peer review and involved patients and carers in agreeing scores for performance under the seven pillars of clinical governance, which then fed into the star-ratings. The drawbacks of continuing this process would have been four-year gaps between visits, limits to the breadth and depth of scrutiny of each visit, and issues of consistency in scoring.

The main features of the Healthcare Commission's annual health check were that trusts determined their scores from self-assurance and there was a risk-based approach to inspections founded on routinely available data. The Healthcare Commission's method offered wide coverage of each trust with annual assessments, but raised concerns about the reliability of those assessments.

Although independent, both the CHI and the Healthcare Commission had only limited leverage over providers as the power to impose sanctions was reserved for the Secretary of State for Health. The recent review by the Department of Health of arm's-length bodies for health and social care concluded that the CQC 'will continue to inspect providers against essential levels of safety and quality in a targeted and risk-based way, taking into account information it receives about a provider…[from]… a range of sources' (Department of Health 2010e, p 17). This is, in effect, continuing to develop the Healthcare Commission's method of self-assurance and its risk-based approach to inspections, which has notable flaws (Bevan and Cornwell 2006; Bevan 2008).

Self-assurance relies on trust boards prioritising issues of clinical quality and safety. The CHI's review of acute services found that boards tended to be well informed on performance with regard to waiting times and finance, but needed better access to information on quality of services and the factors that affect quality (Commission for Health Improvement 2004b, p 18).

At Mid Staffordshire, the board's failure to engage with issues of clinical quality and safety was at the heart of its problems:

> *There were many complaints from patients and relatives about the quality of nursing care. These primarily related to patients not being fed, call bells not being answered, patients left in soiled bedding, medication not being administered, charts not being completed, poor hygiene and general disregard for privacy and dignity. Worryingly, the trust's board appeared to be largely unaware of these.* (Healthcare Commission 2009a, p 8)

Furthermore, a risk-based approach to inspections is handicapped by inadequacies in the data that are routinely available.

Despite its regulatory failures, the Healthcare Commission remained convinced that its system, based on self-assurance with local scrutiny and risk-based and random inspections, was 'the right thing for the regulator to do' (Healthcare Commission 2009b, p 25) and that although some 'thought that they could game the system', 'the breadth of the existing data held and analysed by the Commission, and the importance of the commentaries from patients' groups and local authorities, have steadily caused a change in such attitudes' (Healthcare Commission 2009b, p 25).

Sadly, these assertions were unfounded with regard to Mid Staffordshire: information on what was going wrong was contained within the trust. If a four-yearly rolling programme of CGRs had continued, Mid Staffordshire would have been expecting a review team to visit in 2006/7, the period when so much damage was done.

One strength of CGRs was that this process enabled patients and their relatives to express concerns, and created a safe environment for 'whistleblowing', allowing doctors, nurses and other professionals to report their concerns in confidence to their peers on the review team. It seems inconceivable that under these circumstances the problems at Mid Staffordshire could have been kept from such a team.

Effective regulation of the quality of care of publicly owned providers, which will continue to dominate supply even with pluralism of delivery, requires a rolling programme of inspections based on visits (Bevan and Cornwell 2006; Bevan 2008). The system of CGRs could offer a model, but would require development to learn from evaluations of that process: the seven pillars would need to be reworked; inspections would need to be proportionate; and the system of surveillance would continue to need development (Bardsley *et al* 2009).

The coalition government rejected that model and planned to regulate providers by continuing with self-assurance and risk-based inspections (Department of Health 2010a). As this chapter was going to press, however, Cynthia Bower, the Chief Executive of CQC, announced that CQC plans to abandon this form of 'light touch' regulation for a system of unannounced inspections based on visits. She argued that 'there's no substitute for getting on to the wards and seeing what's going on, talking to patients, talking to clinical staff' (Santry 2011). This change from the government's plan requires extra funding and will be much more difficult for CQC to do than for CHI, because of the scope and scale of CQC's regulatory functions.

Publicly funded health services in England now face the combination of severe fiscal pressures, organisational turmoil, and the challenges of regulating quality with pluralism in delivery. The English NHS of the 2000s, where performance was driven by 'star ratings' and regulation of quality of care by CGRs, will look like a golden age in comparison.

8 Local implementation of New Labour's market reforms

Anna Dixon and Lorelei Jones

Theories of policy process recognise that policy implementation is as important as, if not more important than, policy design in determining the impact a policy has in practice. Unfortunately, policy-makers often do not pay adequate attention to implementation, considering it the responsibility of others, such as managers, and assuming that implementation is simply 'a matter of carrying out that which has been decided upon' (Grindle and Thomas 1991). Studies of policy implementation have highlighted how policies are mediated by features of the local context (Pawson and Tilley 1997). The views and actions of local actors involved in implementation, in particular, have been found to influence the impact of policies (Lipsky 1980).

Policy-makers and politicians tend to focus on the grand ideas, often failing to acknowledge that, although they have the power to enact policies and legislation, they have much less control over how these are put into practice, or the fact that the results of implementation are often quite different from those that were intended or anticipated.

A useful analogy is that policy-makers sit in the control room (Westminster and Whitehall) pulling levers (making policy), but failing to notice that not all the wires are connected (there are no or few mechanisms to make change happen) and that, even where they are, it takes longer than they expect before the mechanisms act (there are lags between the introduction of national policy and local action).

This makes evaluating health reforms all the more challenging. Attributing any observed effect to a particular policy is difficult, especially when reforms are often multifaceted, operate at multiple levels (system, local, organisational, clinical and service), are 'entangled in complex, inherently political processes', and subject to frequent change (Van Eyk *et al* 2001).

Previous research on the internal market during the 1990s found that despite large-scale structural reforms, the measurable impact was modest, partly because the system was constrained by pre-existing institutions, and partly because the 'dose' was too small to have had a marked effect (Le Grand *et al* 1998). Other observers have suggested that the lack of effect is to be expected in a 'complex system' such as the National Health Service (NHS) (Davies 2002).

Previous chapters in this book have discussed briefly the process and extent of the implementation of particular policies. This chapter considers in more detail how the market reforms introduced by the Labour government were implemented locally. Specifically, it discusses the following questions:

- Was there a grand policy design or blueprint for the reforms?

- Was implementation 'big bang' or more gradual and incremental?

- Did these policies replace previous policies or did they add to pre-existing ones?

- Were the policies implemented as intended?

- What was the impact of context on implementation?

This chapter is intended to complement the other chapters in this book by focusing on the contexts and mechanisms that influence the outcomes and impact of policies. The evidence is drawn from studies that have included qualitative methods of data collection, such as ethnographies and extended case studies. One of the particular strengths of qualitative methods in policy evaluation lies in revealing the experiences and views of local actors, and thereby contributing directly to understanding the nature of policy implementation. Crucially, the inclusion of qualitative methods enables evaluations to consider not just 'does the policy work?' but also '*how* does it work (or not)?' (Pawson and Tilley 1997).

An emergent reform package

Although the *NHS Plan* (Department of Health 2000b) was heralded as a 10-year plan for the NHS, it did not set out a blueprint for the market reforms that were to follow. Instead, it was very largely an old-style input plan for the NHS, concentrating on increasing staffing and the capacity to provide services. The details of the market-related policy emerged only gradually. Indeed, the policies were not articulated as a 'package' until 2005 (Department of Health 2005a).

The gradual emergence of the market reforms as a package can partly be explained by the shifting objectives and goals among senior policy advisers and politicians, particularly in the run up to and after the 2001 election. In the second term of the Labour government, it was clear that the priority was to reduce waiting times for elective surgery, but despite spending more on the NHS, the system was not responding commensurately, causing frustration (Le Grand 2007; Powell *et al* 2011). Some of the proposals, such as giving control of budgets to primary care trusts (PCTs) and establishing independent-sector treatment centres (ISTCs), were in the 2001 Labour manifesto, but the more radical ideas for market reform had to wait for the innocuously titled *Delivering the NHS Plan* (Department of Health 2002a). The title suggested that it was simply another post-NHS Plan implementation document, although the new policy package was described by one policy maker as 'the internal market with knobs on' (Powell *et al* 2011, p 87).

It was not until as late as 2005 that the market-based policies were presented explicitly as 'a coherent and mutually supporting set of reforms, which together provide systems and incentives to drive improvements in health and health services' (Department of Health 2005a, p 9). The logic was that the impact would result from the combined effects of the different policies – the benefits would be 'realised through the interactions between all four elements' (Department of Health 2005a, p 12), namely changes to commissioning and patient choice, provider diversity, Payment by Results (PbR), and quality and financial regulation.

This *post hoc* description appears to have been driven by the needs of a new Secretary of State, Patricia Hewitt. The Department of Health was struggling to give a clear and cogent account of the reforms and what they were aiming to achieve (Powell *et al* 2011), and one senior policy-maker admitted that the lack of a unified narrative earlier in the reform process had hampered implementation: 'Not enough thinking had been done about how it all fits together and therefore the right sequencing, pace of development and implementation. So it did feel a bit like a rescue act' (Powell *et al* 2011, p 89).

Thus although presented as a package of mutually reinforcing policies, the market reforms in fact emerged gradually under the Labour government and a succession of secretaries of state for health. As others before have described it, policy-making is not a logical or rational process of decision-making but a much messier process (Heclo 1974). This has repercussions for implementation, to which we now turn.

The sequencing of implementation

Partly due to the evolution of the policy proposals, different elements of the reforms were implemented at different times, and implementation of the specific policies was also staggered.

Demand-side reforms (PCTs and practice-based commissioning [PBC]) were introduced after supply-side reforms, and their implementation was significantly delayed by the 2006 restructuring of PCTs, which reduced their number from 300 to 152 (Exworthy *et al* 2009).

The consequences of the sequencing of the reforms were acknowledged by policy-makers involved in the reforms:

> 'There is a real risk in uneven or very differently paced developments. My perception was that supply side reforms had been more advanced and were picked up more quickly [than] the demand side, which would have been reversed in an ideal world' (policy-maker). (Powell *et al* 2011, p 102)

> 'One of the well rehearsed criticisms is that one should have sorted out commissioning before doing any of the supply side stuff. In the abstract one can see the attractions

of that argument. In practice there are a series of political problematics... and the first was around waiting times' (policy-maker). (Powell *et al* 2011, p 103)

While some felt that commissioning should have been developed and strengthened before giving the provider-side greater autonomy by establishing foundation trusts and stronger incentives through PbR, others felt that this was an important first step in order to address the pressing political problem of waiting times.

The implementation of the individual elements was also phased. Patient choice was the first element to be introduced, largely as a response to long waiting times for elective surgery. It was first piloted in 2002 among cardiac patients in London who had been waiting for more than six months. In 2006 'choice at the point of referral' extended choice to all planned care, although it was not until 2008 that 'free choice' of provider was introduced, which enabled patients to choose any eligible provider.

Similarly, PbR was introduced initially for a small number of elective procedures in foundation trusts. In 2006, it was extended to elective care in all NHS hospitals, and in 2007 to include non-elective outpatient care and treatment in accident and emergency departments.

The phasing of policy implementation has two important implications. First, it provides an opportunity to refine and adjust policies during implementation. Although there were formal evaluations of patient choice pilots, the government did not wait for the results of these before announcing the extension of choice. In a more technical area, such as PbR, learning from the early implementation was used to inform technical refinements of coding and price-setting. The timing of evaluation is therefore important. For example, the effects of competition were only apparent towards the end of the study period, ie, it took three to four years for the combined impact of the market-related policy instruments to have their predicted effect (by about 2007/8) but not before (Cooper *et al* 2011; Gaynor *et al* 2011). If the evaluation had been carried out too soon, the reforms would have been thought to have had no impact.

Second, it means that not all the elements of the market reforms were operating simultaneously or to the same extent throughout the period of implementation. This can have advantages for evaluation, as it allows the impacts of specific elements of the reforms to be isolated to some extent (eg, using interrupted time series analysis and comparative study designs). However, when considering the overall impact of the reforms, it means that there is only a relatively short period for the reforms as a whole to have had an effect. The impact of policy depends on the dose of the mechanism required to effect change. As one policy-maker interviewed in the study by Powell *et al* (2011, p 99) observed: "'Because of the time delay in getting the market based reforms in place, you wouldn't expect them to have had the same degree of impact, nor have they done so in my view" (policy-maker)'.

This quote also suggests that policy-makers were frustrated at the time it took and the speed of change. Even when a policy has officially been implemented, it may not have taken full effect because the dose is weaker or variable between areas. An evaluation of patient choice (Dixon *et al* 2010a) found that only about half of patients recalled being offered a choice, concluding that choice had not been fully implemented, at least not as reflected in government targets, eg, that 90 per cent of referrals should be booked via Choose and Book (dropped from the 2011/12 operating framework). Providers interviewed in the study thought it would take time for choice to develop and that things might change in future, particularly as patients became more aware of choice, more information on the quality of providers became available, and a tighter funding environment heightened competition between providers (Dixon *et al* 2010a). It is therefore possible that the evaluation was not able to detect much impact, not because it was not having any but because the dose was too small.

Layering

As well as the issue of phasing, another complication for any evaluation of reforms is that new policies are often overlaid on existing policies. This was recognised by one of the chief architects of the market-based reforms, who described three overlapping phases of New Labour's reforms: increased supply of staff and modernised infrastructure; national targets and performance management from 1998 onwards; and the reintroduction of competition from 2002/3 (Stevens 2004).

Throughout the period of the market reforms analysed in this book (2002/3– 2009/10), the machinery of government and the NHS (eg, strategic health authorities) was still geared towards ensuring that nationally defined targets were met. This was reflected at the highest level in the public service agreement targets negotiated by the Department of Health with the Treasury and monitored by the Prime Minister's Delivery Unit; as well as, at the Department of Health, in the annual operating framework, which was used by strategic health authorities (and Monitor for foundation trusts) to manage the performance of boards and chief executives. Local accounts of the reforms reflect this layering of policies.

A study of two local health economies (Exworthy *et al* 2009) found that managers were working in a context of multiple policies. The result was a dilution of managerial energy and a diversion of attention to the most pressing concerns, which, for all the organisations involved was achieving national targets, especially those with regard to financial balance, waiting times and infection control.

Exworthy *et al* (2009) found that the prioritisation of national targets not only diverted attention away from implementing market-based policies, but in some cases directly impeded them. For example, the menu of possible choices setting out where patients could opt to receive care was restricted to those providers that were compliant with the 18-week access target. One clinician in the study admitted that in these circumstances the clinicians involved simply reverted to the previous system of manual referrals:

> 'We will offer a patient five places to go and appointment times at those five places. That's what it says. It doesn't mean it's going to be within your county, or within your district, it's anywhere within the country. So all [the general practitioners seeking to refer a patient] does is she logs out of the Choose & Book screen and writes me a letter and sends it in… so that's all that's happening. There is no choice. Patients don't want choice, patients want to be treated in their local hospital' (Clinical director, Hospital). (Exworthy et al 2009, p 127)

Similar findings have been reported elsewhere (Dixon et al 2010a; Powell et al 2011). When asked what drove service improvements within their organisations, providers mentioned a wide array of factors, but choice appeared to have played a relatively minor role (Dixon et al 2010a, p 134). Powell et al, for example, reported that 'access targets were perceived as the highest priority' (Powell et al 2011, p 133). For those working in particular clinical areas, national policies such as national service frameworks were seen to be more influential than the market reforms (Powell et al 2011).

Dissonance

The package of reforms (Department of Health 2005a) was not always well understood at local level (Powell et al 2011). Studies of the local implementation of the market-based policies revealed an unsurprising disconnect between national policy rhetoric, and local experience and interpretation. For example, an ethnographic study by Newman and Vidler found that while individual patient choice of place of care was presented as equity-enhancing in national policy documents, this was 'not convincing for those who have to deal with the reality of resource decisions on the ground' (Newman and Vidler 2006, p 205). In this study, commissioners believed that local strategies aimed at reducing health inequalities, either by encouraging people to adopt healthier lifestyles or by targeting resources at particular groups, were undermined by the emphasis on consumer choice in national policy documents.

Newman and Vidler also found that local clinicians interpreted national policy according to their professional values and aims. Thus, patient choice was reconceptualised by local clinicians as involving patients in decisions about their treatment in the interests of more effective health outcomes. This is illustrated in the following extract from one of the interviews in the study:

> If you talk about choice, how a lot of people will think is that it is about choosing whether you go to this hospital or that hospital. But from my point of view it is around choice right down to the patient level, and it is a bit greater than what

hospital you go to, it's around how do you want the service delivered to you… There are options available for treatment; which one fits you best? (Newman and Vidler 2006, p 205)

With regard to their overall findings, Newman and Vidler commented:

This is not a case of professional refusal or resistance to the government imperative, but can be understood as a more positive attempt to appropriate elements of consumerist discourse in order to secure the professional goals of improved health outcomes. Such outcomes were to be supported through enabling patients to make informed treatment choices, enhancing their expertise and finding ways to make them more 'responsible' for their own health. (Newman and Vidler 2006, p 205)

Similar findings have been reported elsewhere. For example, Powell *et al* found that commissioners and general practitioners (GPs) had interpreted patient choice policy in terms of 'redesign programmes and services based more on "personalisation", self management and coproduction' rather than as a means of promoting competition (Powell *et al* 2011, p 107).

One way in which local actors respond to a rapidly changing policy environment is by relabelling existing initiatives as new policy (Curry *et al* 2008). Relabelling enables local actors to demonstrate that their plans are consistent with national policy direction while meeting local objectives and ensuring the continuation of pre-reform initiatives. Curry *et al* (2008), for example, found that service developments already under way had been reclassified as resulting from PBC, which made it difficult to attribute any developments specifically to PBC.

In a study of PBC, Coleman *et al* (2009) identified two different views of what PBC was intended to achieve:

- for groups themselves to redesign services
- or to encourage use of a wider range of providers.

It was the first interpretation that was the most widespread among local actors. This is perhaps not surprising as the original aims were ill-defined, although Curry *et al* summarised them as:

- to encourage clinical engagement in service redesign and development
- to bring about better, more convenient, services for patients
- to enable better use of resources (Curry *et al* 2008, p viii).

Curry *et al* (2008) found that GPs were more interested in using their budgets to bring about small-scale changes to services rather than commissioning services from different providers.

In a number of studies (Farrar *et al* 2007; Exworthy *et al* 2009; Dixon *et al* 2010a; Powell *et al* 2011), the market-based policies were perceived by local actors as conflicting with the local objective of maintaining a sustainable health economy. For example, the national evaluation of PbR found that:

> *...issues of NHS culture and behavioural norms were raised by the interviewees, as affecting their responses to the incentives of the new system. For instance, a number of interviewees would not pursue greater revenues through increased supply if this was an action considered detrimental to the financial status of the commissioner and the local health economy as a whole.* (Farrar *et al* 2007, p 15)

Concern for the viability of other organisations and the health economy as a whole also led to agreements between organisations not to compete for services but rather to 'carve up' the market so that they were offering different but complementary services (Exworthy *et al* 2009; Dixon *et al* 2010a).

Powell *et al* (2011, p 139) found that the economic downturn had resulted in a shift away from competition to a renewed emphasis on collective action between organisations to ensure a sustainable health economy. One PCT, for example, was refusing to pay using tariff and had told the acute trusts:

> *"'whatever the level the activities are, we cannot afford to pay you, so we're not going to pay you." ...once it becomes clear that they're not going to get paid anymore it then becomes "how do we work with you in order to minimise financial pressure and minimise demand?"'* (PCT director).

Unforeseen consequences

Studies of implementation of the market reforms have revealed both positive and negative impacts that were unforeseen by those who designed the policies (*see* Chapter 9). At least some of this is a consequence of how the policy was interpreted and implemented locally. For example, PbR has been blamed for a number of negative consequences, including:

- a growth in emergency admissions (although the empirical evidence does not support this view)

- so-called upcoding of procedures

- preventing the transfer of care to community settings (Audit Commission and Healthcare Commission 2008; Blunt *et al* 2010; Powell *et al* 2011).

Although PbR was originally designed to increase activity in an effort to reduce waiting times, its extension from elective to emergency admissions, and to medical as well as surgical admissions, created incentives for hospitals to increase activity in areas where this might not be desirable from a quality perspective. At least part of the effect is attributable to the way in which local organisations responded to policies and the incentives they created, and individual behaviours within those organisations.

The way patient choice was implemented was also not as intended. Greener and Mannion (2009b) found that one trust's perception of the Choose and Book computerised booking system was that it was useful not so much to help it compete for business within the new economy of care, but rather as a way of dealing with excess demand for its services.

Some commissioners introduced referral management centres, partly in order to support the delivery of patient choice targets (that all patients should be offered a choice of at least four or five providers and that a specific proportion of referrals be made through Choose and Book). Ironically, referral management centres have also been found to restrict patient choice by directing referrals to particular providers, for example, to make use of local ISTCs when their capacity had already been paid for by the PCT (Imison and Naylor 2010; Co-operation and Competition Panel 2011).

Although few patients used published information to make a choice of provider, and few providers reported competing directly for patients, the threat that patients could go elsewhere did seem to stimulate a greater focus on the patient experience (Dixon *et al* 2010a). This effect was not created, however, by choice but rather stemmed from providers' concerns about their reputation and a desire to retain the loyalty of local patients.

Other policies had unintended benefits. For example, an unexpected finding from a study by Coleman *et al* (2009) of PBC was a new willingness among GPs to undertake peer review and performance management of each other's work. This took the form of practice visits to discuss performance, publication of named performance data, open discussion of performance data in meetings, and the use of PBC as a mechanism to implement an unrelated performance assessment framework.

Interestingly, the coalition government now plans to strengthen GP involvement in commissioning. At least one of the explicit intentions behind this policy is to promote peer scrutiny of performance in general practice (Goodwin *et al* 2011).

Local context

The extent to which market-based policies were implemented varied across sites and specialties. Contextual features influencing implementation included the local configuration of providers, their proximity to each other, the type of services they provided, and the nature of pre-existing relationships. The reforms were not painted on to a blank canvas, but implemented where there were existing local structures, relationships, values and aims.

This is illustrated by the findings of a two-year ethnographic study that explored the local implementation of patient choice policy (Greener and Mannion 2009b). The study focused on an NHS trust that operated on the fringes of a conurbation where there was easy access to several providers of care and therefore considerable potential for a health care market to develop. The study found that existing referral patterns within the local area were extremely sticky (ie, resistant to change), even when they did not appear to be entirely rational. For example, referrals were not always to either the closest or the highest-rated local care provider. Instead, they were based on historical GP–consultant relationships. Patients were also 'extremely loyal to the hospital, and believed that it was part of their community' (Greener and Mannion 2009b, p 98), although a view prevailed among trust managers that it was the GPs, rather than patients, who were the real customers of the hospital, and this does appear to have been borne out by the evidence (Dixon *et al* 2010a).

Similarly, Dixon *et al* (2010a) describe a local health economy with one dominant trust to which patients were extremely loyal. It was primarily concerned with managing demand for its services and, rather than competing with other providers, it actively sought to encourage patients to go elsewhere to reduce pressure on its own facilities.

At other sites, Dixon *et al* (2010a) found that providers competed for patients at the boundaries of their catchment areas. These were often rural areas where patients were equidistant from several hospitals, and is consistent with the quantitative analyses reported in Chapter 6 that found the largest increases in competition to be in such areas. This study also found that some hospital providers felt threatened when local commissioners were tendering more aggressively for services and hospitals were having to compete with the private sector.

Exworthy *et al* (2009) concluded that the persistence of earlier social and institutional relationships meant that the market-based policies did not have their intended effects. For example, patient loyalty to the local hospital, and a reluctance to destabilise local organisations, meant that referral patterns were maintained and local providers negotiated market share. Conversely, market-based policies could also disrupt local social and institutional relationships and produce unintended consequences, such as by creating an adversarial environment that prevented necessary collaboration and produced inefficiencies by diminishing trust.

Market reforms were also not seen as appropriate to some specialties. Powell *et al* (2011) found that among both commissioners and providers, there was a commonly held view that patient choice did not have much relevance in long-term chronic conditions such as diabetes. In these conditions, greater value was placed on best-practice guidance, such as that contained in national service frameworks, as a lever for improving services; and the patient's voice, particularly in making decisions about treatment, was regarded as more relevant than choice of provider or place of care:

In most sites it was acknowledged that the majority of patients would wish to choose their local hospital out of convenience. Where multiple entry points to diabetes care existed (particularly for secondary care) it was reported that this had the potential to fragment, or undermine, the potential to develop a pathway of care. (Powell et al 2011, p 182)

Discussion and conclusions

There was no blueprint for these reforms. Instead, the various elements of the reform programme emerged gradually, which meant there was some difficultly in articulating the reforms clearly and explaining how the different components interacted. This overarching narrative emerged relatively late in the day and may explain why local actors were often unclear about what and how the reforms were supposed to operate.

The staged approach to both the development and implementation of the market reforms by the Labour government meant that some aspects of the reforms moved ahead more quickly than others. Although this had some advantages – giving the opportunity to refine policies such as PbR in the light of feedback and the changing context – there were some down sides. Most critically, the providers were able to seize their new freedoms in response to stronger incentives before the commissioners had had time to develop their skills or approaches to manage demand. One consequence of the sequencing and layering described here is that it may have limited the extent to which any impact is observable – the full set of reforms were only in play for a relatively short period towards the end of New Labour's time in office as a result of the time-lag between policy enactment and implementation.

Despite a commitment to the market reforms among politicians and leading policy advisers, implementation of the reforms alongside existing top-down performance management of targets limited the extent to which they took hold locally. For local leaders, the imperative to meet national targets remained, and for clinicians working in areas outside elective surgery other policy initiatives appeared more salient.

In some localities, including urban areas, the market structure (eg, one dominant trust across several sites) and lack of population mobility meant that choice and competition were not seen to be relevant or did not amount to a significant change as there might well have been de facto a choice of hospital for many years. Prior assumptions that choice was not so relevant or feasible in rural areas were in fact found to be wrong. Surprisingly, the choice of provider and competition for patients was greater in rural areas where no single provider dominated and people were more used to travelling to access services (Dixon *et al* 2010a; Gaynor *et al* 2011).

The research studies reviewed here found a degree of dissonance between national policy rhetoric and its understanding by local implementers. As a result, policies conceived of nationally did not necessarily have the desired impact, indeed some had unintended consequences, not all of which were negative. In line with much of the literature on policy implementation, local implementers had significant discretion to interpret the policies locally. Although some may argue that this is a good thing, allowing innovation and adaptation to local circumstances, in some cases people carried on as before, simply rebranding existing activities, or resisted them entirely.

The experience of market reforms points to a need for policy architects to recognise that local actors, context and institutions will mediate any changes. It suggests a need to pay more attention to the implementation phase of policy, and to identify what can be done to increase the chances of any policy having its intended impact.

9 Assessing and explaining the impact of New Labour's market reforms

Nicholas Mays and Anna Dixon

This chapter summarises the evidence assembled in the previous chapters covering different aspects of the market-related reforms of the English National Health Service (NHS) under New Labour. It tries to assess the extent to which the objectives of the reforms had been met or the concerns of sceptics vindicated by the time that New Labour lost power in May 2010. It concludes by discussing the nature of the evidence available and the challenges of evaluating large-scale, complex, system-level changes against a background of ongoing policy initiatives, parallel policy developments and a large increase in the financial and real resources available to the NHS.

Objectives of the reforms

From analysis of the policy documents discussed in Chapter 1, the main objectives of the market-related changes to the English NHS introduced gradually with effect from financial year 2002/3 can be distilled as follows:

- to improve efficiency, particularly in the acute hospital sector for elective treatment, by paying hospitals using fixed (benchmark) prices per episode, allowing NHS hospitals greater managerial and financial freedom, and encouraging competition between NHS and independent hospitals for individual patients and for contracts from commissioners (competition in and for the NHS market)

- to improve quality, particularly in the acute hospital sector for elective treatment, by encouraging fixed-price, quality-driven competition involving both NHS and independent hospitals, by refining the system of quality regulation of providers and by commissioners tendering for new and innovative models of service

- to improve the responsiveness of acute hospital services (eg, shorter waiting times and better patient experience) by introducing individual patient choice of any willing provider, primarily for elective surgery and diagnostic services, and by paying hospitals for individual episodes of care so that the money followed the patients rather than patient referrals having to follow previously agreed contracts with specific providers

- to increase the rate of clinical and organisational innovation (and thereby improve the quality and efficiency of care) in acute hospitals by allowing high-performing NHS hospitals greater managerial and financial freedom (including the ability to retain surpluses for investment), and by encouraging entry of independent providers to the NHS market, especially for elective surgery

- to increase output (treatment rates) in the acute hospital sector, thereby enabling faster access to treatment, by paying hospitals using fixed prices per unit of output so that, in theory, the more work they did, the more income they received

- to improve socio-economic equity of access by offering individual choice of place of elective care to all NHS patients, not just those able to afford the option of private-sector care as well as NHS care

- to reduce unnecessary demand for hospital care and to develop innovative alternatives to hospitalisation by giving more influence over primary care trust (PCT) commissioning to primary care professionals, especially general practitioners (GPs), through practice-based commissioning (PBC) in which volunteer practices were given an indicative budget by the PCT to be used to commission selected services for their patients.

The key elements in the reforms – entry of independent sector providers, individual patient choice of provider, and output-based hospital reimbursement, so-called Payment by Results (PbR) – were introduced gradually (*see* Chapter 1 and the chapters covering specific reform mechanisms for more details), but were all in place by January 2006, which can therefore be regarded as the date from which the reforms were more or less fully operative (Cooper *et al* 2010). However, they were not described officially as an interrelated package of changes until 2005 (Department of Health 2005a), and free choice of any provider was introduced only in 2008. As a result of the phased implementation and lags in availability of data, the evidence on the effects of the New Labour market reforms considered in this book comes in the main from only three years of fully implemented reforms, 2006/7–2008/9.

Concerns about the reforms

Inevitably, a set of changes designed to make the English NHS operate more like an ordinary consumer market – albeit one with public finance, considerable restrictions on market entry, close financial and managerial regulation, and national level political oversight and accountability – was bound to excite concerns among critical commentators. As described in greater detail in Chapters 1 and 6, the main problems envisaged were the following:

- that the fundamental differences between health care and other markets (eg, the nature of demand, information imbalances between users and providers, the difficulty of assessing the quality of service, barriers to individual and organisational entry, etc) could not be easily circumvented and would prevent effective implementation of a provider market

- that equity of access to health care would be harmed for two contrasting reasons – the offer of individual patient choice would be exploited more effectively by better-off, better-educated, lower-need patients, and the fixed (average) price payment system would encourage discrimination against more costly, higher-need patients

- that competition on the basis of quality rather than price would fail to have the positive effects predicted because there was insufficient robust and easily interpretable information available on the performance of different services and providers, which would therefore allow providers to underinvest in quality-improving initiatives

- that the availability of information on quality of care would be reduced on the grounds of commercial confidentiality in an increasingly competitive market environment involving more private sector players

- that the notion of a provider market driven partly by individual patient choice of provider was based on a misunderstanding of what the majority of NHS patients wanted: they were not interested in shopping around for care, particularly when compromised by ill-health, wanting instead guaranteed access to high-quality local services and being more interested in choosing the type of care than the organisation providing the care

- that the emphasis on implementing a market within the NHS would leave no room for the articulation of the collective, as opposed to individual, preferences necessary to shape a public service paid for from general taxation and delivered locally

- that any decisions about the nature and location of major infrastructure such as hospitals and information technology would be better taken through co-ordinated national and/or regional planning processes, but that these would become impossible in a competitive market, leading to inefficient use of capital, service duplication and inefficiencies as a result of a lack of concentration of services in specialised settings.

Even some of those who could see the potential advantages of encouraging greater patient choice and provider competition had concerns that the reforms were unduly focused on acute hospital services, and that even within the acute sector, the reforms might work well only for the minority of elective (planned) services where individual patient choice and PbR could conceivably interact to produce desirable forms of inter-hospital competition.

There was therefore a risk that competition for electives could weaken the financial position of a hospital and put at risk access to the emergency services that were essential to the local population. There was also a risk that provider competition might prevent the sort of collaboration between primary and secondary care that was increasingly being seen as the way to improve the care of people with complex, long-term health problems.

In addition, there were the perennial concerns that the changes did little or nothing to empower the commissioners (purchasers) of services (eg, PBC groups would be too small and insufficiently skilled to drive the major service reconfigurations needed to rebalance care away from hospitals) and, if anything, the combination of more autonomous providers in the shape of foundation trusts and payment for activity through PbR would further weaken their position *vis-à-vis* the hospitals.

Irrespective of whether they were for or against the changes, many commentators were also concerned that market-like reforms would pose a major challenge to elected politicians, especially in a Westminster system of government, in following through the logic of markets, which is that inevitably some providers will fail or get into financial difficulties, incurring public disapproval and resistance. The experience of the less radical 1990s internal market in the NHS had been that politicians had intervened to dampen down the impact of market competition precisely where it threatened to bring about significant change in the configuration of hospitals in London. Given the very high political and media profile of the NHS, especially of its hospitals, there seemed few reasons to believe that a similar dynamic would not operate under New Labour.

The next two sections summarise the extent to which New Labour's objectives were met and whether the problems foreseen by critics and sceptics materialised, looking, in turn, at the degree to which the reforms were implemented and the effects of the changes on the performance of the system.

Extent of implementation of the reforms

How far were the reforms put in place? By the time New Labour left office in May 2010, the English NHS was still some distance away from functioning as a fully-fledged provider market for publicly financed care. The system continued to be run by a closely managed hierarchy, while operating in a more market-like way in specific respects. This is scarcely surprising given the tenacity of past relationships and behaviours in all systems under change (Greener and Mannion 2009b), and the relative novelty of the changes in the period studied. For example, PbR required the development and implementation of a completely new way of paying for a large percentage of the hospital services delivered to NHS patients.

Turning first to consider what had changed, there were many indications that the English NHS was operating more like a market:

- the independent sector was more routinely involved in the provision of services to NHS patients, most notably in elective surgery (*see* Chapter 2)

- an increasing proportion of NHS provider organisations was becoming foundation trusts, operating with less ministerial direction and more financial autonomy (Chapter 2)

- half of elective patients reported being offered a choice of provider at the point of referral (Chapter 4)

- by some measures and in some areas, there was greater potential competition between acute hospitals for elective services (Chapter 6)

- reimbursement of providers on the basis of healthcare resource groups (HRGs) under PbR accounted for approximately 40 per cent of the hospital care bought by PCTs (Smith and Charlesworth 2011) (Chapter 5)

- PCTs were devolving parts of their budgets to practice-based commissioners to enable them to take better-informed commissioning decisions that were more closely attuned to the needs of their patients than PCTs could (Chapter 3)

- the quality regulator (the Care Quality Commission [CQC]), the financial regulator of NHS foundation trusts (Monitor) and the Competition and Co-operation Panel were beginning to work together to ensure a more level playing field between public, private and third-sector providers of NHS services based on their ability to provide good-quality services (CQC) at the NHS tariff price and their financial viability (Monitor) (Chapter 7).

Such changes also appeared to be altering the management culture of hospitals in the NHS during the period, from a dominant clan culture towards a more competitive, externally focused, rational one (Mannion *et al* 2009), implying that some of the externally mandated changes were having a more profound effect on NHS-owned organisations.

In contrast, there was also evidence of continuity and the limits to change, such as the modest extent to which services were subject to market forces, the continuing salience of previous, non-market policies, and the persistence of long-standing behaviours that were at variance with market incentives. As described in Chapter 8, the market reforms represented but one layer of policy, and co-existed throughout the second half of the 2000s with very different models of service improvement, sometimes leading to diversion and dilution of management effort.

More specifically, the entry and growth of new providers was limited and had been relatively slow (eg, just under 2 per cent of NHS elective activity was provided by the independent-sector treatment centres (ISTCs) by 2007/8 (Audit Commission and Healthcare Commission 2008) (Chapter 2), and overall the hospital market remained fairly concentrated (Chapter 6). This was reinforced by the tendency of GPs to continue to exercise choice on behalf of their patients and for patients, with the help of their GPs, largely to continue to choose local providers that they knew. Patients were typically offered only a few options and were generally not aware that they could choose a private provider by right (Chapter 4).

Hospital managers identified GPs as more important for patient referrals than the newly empowered patients, and focused their marketing accordingly (Chapter 8).

They also reported that waiting times and financial targets loomed far larger than the incentives theoretically generated by the NHS market.

Concentration was also reinforced by national initiatives in a number of service areas to plan referral patterns and care at a regional level in order to improve patient outcomes. For example, in critical care and care for patients with heart disease, stroke and cancer, efforts had been made to ensure that a higher proportion of patients was treated at fewer, more specialised, regional centres with higher throughput and potentially better outcomes (Darzi 2007).

Implementation of the market-related changes therefore also varied by specialty and by area, with a stronger market focus on elective care (Chapter 8) than on other specialties. This was partly because the chosen model of market reform, particularly the use of activity-driven payment of hospitals, appeared to fit elective hospital services – such as surgery and diagnostics – much better than it did other service areas, and to operate more strongly in locations where there was more potential or actual competition between providers (Chapters 6 and 8). By contrast, services such as those for people with mental health problems and community health services (eg, district nursing) appeared relatively untouched by the market changes and remained outside the PbR system (Chapters 5 and 8). The goal of extending PbR to the majority of hospital services was far from being met (Chapter 5), and the share of NHS spending covered by PbR had altered little since 2006/7 (Smith and Charlesworth 2011).

Likewise, the reforms were seen as marginal by those working in places where there was a monopoly provider and a history of collaborative working relationships (Chapter 8). The approach to competition and hospital payment adopted by New Labour was also seen as irrelevant to improving the care of people with more complex and longer-term conditions, for which better co-ordination of care between providers, especially across the primary–secondary care divide, was increasingly seen as important (Curry and Ham 2010) but hampered by PbR (Chapter 5).

Waiting-time targets remained in place as reminders of the persistence of New Labour's successful pre-market policies of centralised objective-setting backed by tough, hierarchical performance management and of the continuing importance of non-market mechanisms and relationships in maintaining and improving the English NHS (Chapters 4 and 7).

Indeed, the combination of reforms from different periods in the life of the New Labour administrations (so-called layering) seems to have confused local actors and weakened the ability of the NHS at local level to pursue the necessary market-related changes (Chapter 8). In particular, there is evidence that the delivery of national waiting time and financial targets diverted attention and energy from vigorously implementing the later market-based changes and could even have impeded them. It is also clear that local health care system actors frequently faced imperatives that rivalled those related to generating provider competition. For example, on occasion, both commissioners and providers gave priority to the financial and clinical health of the wider health care system rather than competing with one another, and there was increasing evidence towards the end of New Labour's term in office of organisations in local health economies working together rather than competing in order to ensure their survival in hard financial times (Chapter 8).

Finally, there was evidence of an imbalance in the implementation of the different elements in the reforms, with developments in commissioning (with the exception of individual patient choice of place of elective care) lagging behind the rest. Right at the end of the period, there were reports that commissioners' performance against the Department of Health's world class commissioning criteria was improving (NHS Confederation 2010), but, for most of the time, PCTs were widely seen as the weakest link in the system (Chapter 3). For example, the progress and achievements of PCTs and, in particular, of PBC schemes appeared to be limited to small-scale, somewhat marginal changes in local health services when assessed in relation to the main challenges facing the NHS, such as large-scale hospital service redesign and reducing reliance on hospital services. On the other hand, commissioning underwent near-continuous reorganisation while the other market mechanisms were being rolled out, making it difficult for the commissioning organisations to make a concerted impact. Commissioners also struggled to manage spending since they lacked control over clinical decisions such as GP referrals.

Given the incompleteness of implementation by 2010, it is not surprising that Brereton and Gubb (2010, p xii) were forced to conclude at the end of the New Labour period, from a free-market perspective: 'We found isolated examples of the NHS market delivering the benefits that were anticipated; however, the market, by and large, has failed thus far to deliver such benefits on any meaningful or systemic scale'.

The modest scale of impact perceived by Brereton and Gubb (2010) is partly attributable to variation in the extent of implementation of the changes in different geographic areas, and to differences between providers in the degree to which the reforms challenged their previous ways of operating. For instance, different providers (predominantly hospitals in this period) provided different service mixes and thus faced differing degrees of exposure to, for example, competition for elective surgical patients to maintain or increase their incomes (Dixon *et al* 2010a).

It is also apparent that implementation of the market reforms played out differently in urban, suburban and rural areas, as well as within local health care systems facing financial difficulties (eg, due to apparent hospital overcapacity) compared with those in better financial circumstances (Chapter 8). For example, the largest increases in spatial competition between hospitals appeared to have occurred in the semi-rural areas between the conurbations rather than in the cities where there had always been considerable de facto choice of providers (Chapter 6).

Implementation of the reforms was further affected at local level by the concerns of patients, commissioners and providers that an excessive focus on competition could destabilise the local health care system (Chapter 8). For example, a focus on short-term competition in the market for elective treatment might be perceived as risking reducing the income of a district acute hospital, thereby threatening its financial viability as a provider of emergency and urgent care to a population reliant on its services. In such circumstances, the already sticky (resistant to short-term change) referral patterns between GPs and hospital specialists might be even less likely to alter in response to opportunities for patient choice and competition for elective care.

Impact of the market reforms versus other changes under New Labour

If the extent to which the market changes had been put in place by 2010 was mixed, what of the evidence of their impact on the efficiency, equity and responsiveness of the system? Did the concerns of critics or the benefits predicted by proponents come to pass?

The evidence presented in the preceding chapters shows broadly that the market-related changes introduced from 2002 by New Labour tended to have the effects predicted by proponents and that most of the feared undesirable impacts had not materialised to any extent, at least by early in 2010. However, the scale of the market-related effects was modest compared with the overall improvements in the performance of the NHS from 1997 associated with other policies, such as service modernisation and targets, and these effects were realised in a benign period of strongly growing NHS spending.

Before and during the period of the staged reintroduction of a provider market into the English NHS, its performance had been improving. Indeed, a large part of the rationale for the revival of supply-side competition in 2002/3 was to sustain and accelerate these already improving trends (Stevens 2004). Advisers close to Prime Minister Tony Blair became convinced that the pressure for further improvement could only come from using new policy instruments alongside those already in place, such as investment, so-called modernisation, and targets.

As a result, many of the gains made before and after 2002/3 were unrelated to competition, patient choice and the rest of the market reform package. Indeed, the predominant narrative on New Labour's period as custodian of the English NHS must focus on the increases in spending and the size of the workforce (eg, 50,000 more doctors and 100,000 more nurses and midwives) after 2000, together with strongly enforced targets, leading to improvements in performance (Bevan and Hood 2006a; Boyle 2011). For example, it is clear from studies comparing the performance of the NHS in England with that in Scotland that the faster waiting-time reductions in England were the result of time-limited, quantified waiting-time targets backed by vigorous performance management (Propper *et al* 2004; Propper *et al* 2008a; Connolly *et al* 2010). Again, hospital activity rates appeared to increase faster in England than in Scotland, but this was observed for services both within and outside the PbR tariff scheme (Farrar *et al* 2009), suggesting that these trends were primarily the result of other non-market policies, particularly the pressure to hit waiting-time targets.

General NHS performance trends

The general indicators of improvement from 1997 onwards that were not necessarily directly related to the market, were:

- major and sustained improvements in waiting lists and waiting times for hospital and primary care services

- a reduction in the rate of the two leading causes of hospital-acquired infection

- a reduction in smoking rates

- better support in primary care for those with chronic conditions, including incentives for GPs to manage patients with chronic conditions

- greatly improved waiting times for cancer diagnosis and treatment, improved access to cost-effective drugs and better post-treatment survival rates for most cancers

- notable improvements in access to cardiac surgery and recommended standards of stroke care contributing to falling mortality for cardiovascular disease

- better access to specialist early intervention and crisis resolution teams for acute mental illness

- increases in overall public satisfaction with the NHS

- reduced infant mortality and longer life expectancy for all social groups, but with progress faster among less deprived groups leading to widening health inequalities (Thorlby and Maybin 2010).

New Labour had made considerably less progress by 2010 in improving the NHS in terms of:

- reducing the harm attributable to the misuse of alcohol and overeating

- reducing avoidable causes of hospital use

- reducing unjustified variations in processes and outcomes of care (eg, in radiotherapy, cardiovascular surgery and stroke care)

- reducing health inequalities between more and less deprived areas and people

- ensuring equitable access to services.

Perhaps the biggest weakness under New Labour lay in the apparent decline in NHS productivity in the 2000s and the substantial scope remaining in the system for more efficient delivery of services. On first inspection, this could be interpreted as an obvious indication that the reintroduction of the market had failed in that the combination of activity-driven payments through PbR and inter-hospital competition, particularly for electives, might have been expected to increase output, reduce unit costs and thence improve productivity. In fact, the fall in measured productivity was largely due to the big increase in NHS funding, leading to more staff and higher wages that were not compensated for by increases in measurable output. In addition, there were higher capital costs and increases in costs associated with requirements for improvements in care (eg, through implementation of national service frameworks and National Institute for Health and Clinical Excellence recommendations) (Boyle 2011).

These increases overwhelmed in scale any potentially positive impact of the NHS market reforms. Furthermore, in most of the period there was little emphasis on raising productivity in return for the additional resources. Instead, the focus was on increasing spending and staffing levels per capita so that they were closer to the European average through old-style input planning.

Specific impact of the market changes

However, far from having failed, the evidence in this book suggests that NHS performance in terms of efficiency and productivity would have been weaker in the absence of New Labour's market reforms. Furthermore, there was also no obvious sign of the market-related changes hampering or reversing the improving trends in other areas of performance. In other words, the reintroduction of a more explicitly pro-competitive approach within the English NHS most likely did help to make better use of the large increase in resources, even though it did not improve productivity enough to offset the resource increases.

The hospital market changes with largely fixed-price competition through activity-based reimbursement together with individual patient choice of place of care for electives did appear to have had some measurable positive effects in the direction predicted from theory and previous experience, particularly in relation to efficiency, and without obviously harming equity of use of services. The evidence for a positive impact on quality (outcomes) is more contentious, although suggestive (*see* below). It is extremely difficult to assess the impacts of individual components of the reforms, particularly the contribution of PCT commissioning and PBC since any effects are mediated by the response of providers to their commissioning strategies.

The clearest evidence of impact is probably that from the evaluation of PbR discussed in Chapter 4, since this study included not only a controlled before and after analysis in England as PbR was extended over time to new specialties and new hospitals, but also longitudinal comparisons between England's NHS with PbR and Scotland's avowedly non-competitive NHS without PbR (Farrar *et al* 2009). The introduction of PbR was associated with reductions in unit costs as indicated by reductions in inpatient length of stay and increases in the proportion of treatment provided as day cases, although the scale of the effects was small. The quality of care, as measured using patient-level administrative data (eg, in-hospital and 30-day mortality rates), was not obviously adversely affected by the introduction of PbR, indicating an overall improvement in efficiency that would not otherwise have occurred.

Despite the widely held view that the incentives in PbR consistently encouraged more hospital investigation and treatment, and inflated recorded levels of activity (Chapters 5 and 8), the evidence is less straightforward. For example, the comparison in 2004/5 of the activity in foundation trusts (subject to PbR) with that of non-foundation trusts (then not yet eligible to use PbR) showed that foundation trusts' spells did not increase relative to those of the non-foundation trusts (Farrar *et al* 2009). It is highly likely that policies other than PbR, such as waiting-time targets, stimulated the growth in the volume of care.

Further key findings from the evidence on the market reforms are that between 2003 and 2010:

- hospitals in areas with market structures where competition was more likely appeared to have experienced faster improvements in patient outcomes as assessed by mortality rates than those in areas with a less potentially competitive market structure, and without increasing their costs (Chapter 6)

- the offer of patient choice of place of elective treatment was made to about half of the eligible patients, was generally valued, seemed to have been made relatively equally to all patient groups (although selection of a non-local hospital was greater among the better educated) and was associated with faster reductions in waiting times in patients from lower socio-economic groups (Chapter 4)

- diverse (non-NHS owned) providers appeared to perform as well as NHS-owned providers, although the amount of evidence on the relative quality and efficiency of services was small (Chapter 2)

- the greater freedom given to NHS foundation trusts appeared to enable them to improve services through faster decision-making and the ability to invest any surpluses, although there was no evidence that the superior performance of foundation trusts compared with that of ordinary NHS trusts related to their status, as they had been chosen to become foundation trusts on the basis of stronger performance (Chapter 2)

- PCTs appeared to be influential in encouraging or discouraging new entrants in the local health system and in how they were managed to produce high-quality care (Chapter 2)

- there was no evidence that socio-economic equity of use of care had been harmed by the changes, at least in terms of the use of common elective services (Cookson et al 2010a, 2010b) (see below for more on equity).

One aspect of the reform package that appeared to have contributed little at system level was the entry of independent-sector providers both of hospital and ambulatory care services (Chapter 2). This was primarily because of the small share of activity provided by the independent sector in the period. As a result of the poor quality of the tendering process for the ISTCs, there is evidence that the NHS paid excessively for treatments, particularly from the first wave of ISTCs, without commensurately higher quality of care (Pollock and Kirkwood 2009).

There were some particularly unexpected effects, most notably that the most marked increase in the potential for competition between hospitals (Chapter 6) and take-up of individual patient choice (Chapter 4) appeared to occur outside the main urban areas rather than within them (this was obvious in retrospect, perhaps, given that there has always been greater scope for choice and potential for competition in the cities). There were also hints in the evidence of a difference between national and local studies, and between those tapping participants' perceptions of change and those using routine quantitative indicators of change. Crudely, the national, quantitative studies tended to show impacts of the reforms in the direction expected (Farrar et al 2009; Cooper et al 2010, 2011; Gaynor et al 2011), whereas more local studies that included qualitative data (Dixon et al 2010a; Powell et al 2011) tended to indicate that the market reforms were far from salient in the minds of many participants, were generally regarded as less important than other policies (particularly waiting time and financial targets), and were extensively critiqued and sometimes resisted. Many local actors emphasised their reluctance to allow competition to disrupt long-standing relationships in the local health care system, and highlighted the value of co-operation and collaboration across the local system as a preferred strategy for managing in a worsening financial environment while maintaining the quality of local services (Chapter 8).

One possible explanation for the differences between different types of studies is that they were differentially sensitive to the effects of other policy changes unrelated to the reintroduction of the market into the English NHS that also affected performance, thus making it very difficult to isolate the contribution of market competition, patient choice and activity-based payment of hospitals from other previous, parallel and later changes. This conjecture is taken up later in the chapter.

Did competition improve quality?

On the face of it, the most striking finding from all the evidence collected on the impact of the reintroduction of the market to the English NHS was that higher levels of potential inter-hospital competition appeared to be associated with a faster reduction in hospital mortality rates (Cooper et al 2011; Gaynor et al 2011).

This has probably been the most discussed and controversial finding from the period as it appears to show a positive effect of scope for competition on quality of care when prices for a proportion of hospital services are fixed under PbR. Research on the 1990s internal market, in which prices were locally determined, showed, by contrast, an association between greater potential competition and higher death rates (Propper *et al* 2008a). The authors of both studies carried out in the setting of New Labour's NHS market regard the contrasting findings from the two decades as a genuine demonstration of the merits of a more competitive health care market, particularly one where prices are fixed rather than negotiated locally. They argue that their findings are consistent with predictions from economic theory and the much larger empirical literature from the United States (Chapter 6).

However, the findings that hospital all-cause mortality and mortality from acute myocardial infarction appear to have improved faster in the latter part of the 2000s in areas with more potential for competition as measured by elective patient flows are puzzling because acute myocardial infarction admissions and treatments are emergencies, whereas New Labour's reinvented market system was meant to be driven by elective patient and GP choice. Why should emergency care be better delivered in potentially more competitive areas when none of the affected patients will have chosen their treatment destination? The authors of both studies point to another study that seems to show that the quality of hospital management is higher in NHS hospitals exposed to higher potential for competition (Bloom *et al* 2010b). They therefore hypothesise that higher-quality hospital management mediates the relationship between competition and lower death rates after emergency treatment across all services in more competitive areas.

The rationale seems to be that hospitals will sharpen their management practices when faced with increased competition or prevailing high levels of competition, and that better-managed hospitals are better both at treating elective and emergency cases because they have more robust systems. These more robust systems can be seen as the product of the higher quality of management in the more competitive areas. Another related possibility is that hospitals in more competitive areas may have taken steps to improve the quality of their elective services in order to retain or increase their market share in the face of PbR, which, in turn, requires changes in the organisation as a whole, affecting the delivery and quality of emergency services such as the treatment of patients with acute myocardial infarction.

While such reasoning is plausible in principle, there is some doubt about whether hospital management and clinical systems could have responded within only three years (the findings cover 2003/4–2007/8) to market policies and related incentives that were not functioning fully until around January 2006 at the earliest, that only applied to 60 per cent of acute hospital income in 2006/7 (Boyle 2007), and that were reported by managers in research interviews as being of only marginal importance compared with other policies such as financial and waiting-time targets (Powell *et al* 2011). In addition, throughout the period of study, the NHS budget was growing rapidly, further taking the edge off competitive pressures.

Unsurprisingly, non-economists would tend to look elsewhere to try to explain these perplexing findings, for example, looking to see whether the results could be explained by patterns of clinical innovation unrelated to competition or the expectation of competition. One possible explanation for the pattern of association observed relates to initiatives taken in the 2000s to regionalise hospital care such as in the case of stroke, coronary heart disease, neonatal intensive care, adult critical care and cancers, all services with appreciable mortality (NHS London 2007; Durand *et al* 2010). In each case, the basic idea was to concentrate the more complex treatments in fewer centres in each regional network. It is plausible that these centres would have been selected on the basis of their previous performance, thereby increasing the proportion of patients treated at the best centres in order to try to improve outcomes. In such a situation, it is possible that improvements in outcomes at hospitals receiving more patients from other districts (ie, apparently competing more successfully for patients) were the result of NHS plans to regionalise services.

The Herfindahl-Hirschman index used to measure the potential level of competition in different areas in both studies is based on patient flow data, albeit for elective care since these were the services most likely to be exposed to choice and competition. A change in referral patterns away from the local hospital is interpreted as an increase in spatial competition. So, the effect observed could be related not so much to competition or increases in competition, but rather to the opposite, a planned attempt to direct patients towards high-quality, high-volume centres. For example, adult critical care was 'networked' and achieved significant improvements in quality (mortality) during the 2000s, but there was no element of market forces/competition for that service (Durand *et al* 2010).

Likewise, acute myocardial infarction mortality (used by both Cooper *et al* 2011 and Gaynor *et al* 2011) risks being confounded as an indicator of the impact of competition and/or increases in competition by the introduction of primary angioplasty (a central policy initiative of the Department of Health), which concentrated care in specific providers with the appropriate expertise. As a result, in England and Wales in 2004, for example, only 5 per cent of acute myocardial infarctions were so treated, but by 2007 this had risen to 20 per cent as a result of clinical and organisational policy change (West *et al* 2011). The number of angioplasties for myocardial infarction increased almost eight-fold between 2003 and 2009 (West *et al* 2011). In a recent extension of their analysis, Gaynor and colleagues have tested whether their findings could have been confounded by such changes in cardiac care (Gaynor *et al* 2011). They find no such effect and, in fact, an indication that the competition effect is stronger when controls are introduced for changes in treatment patterns, reinforcing their original conclusion that greater competition is driving improvements in hospital care.

As well as the direct effects of competition, in a competitive market there is normally a system of regulation designed to encourage high standards and prevent standards from falling below an agreed minimum level. This is particularly important in health care, in which the quality of services is hard to measure and difficult for users to judge. Unfortunately, the evidence on the performance of the rapidly changing series of quality regulators in the 2000s is limited and hard to interpret, but tends to raise doubts about whether the system of quality regulation was capable of assuring patients and the public that competition was on the basis of a guaranteed high basic standard of care (Chapter 7).

Did competition harm equity?

If the reintroduction of a provider market appears to have been associated with improvements in quality and efficiency, this still leaves the risk of widening inequity in the use of services given that PbR gave hospitals incentives to reduce cost for elective surgery (Chapter 5).

Cookson and Laudicella (2011) examined whether hospital patients living in small areas of low socio-economic status cost more to treat in order to see if there were *a priori* grounds to expect so-called cream-skimming. They found that there were potential incentives for competing hospitals to 'cream-skim'. Despite this, they found no obvious change in socio-economic equity of use from 2001/2 to 2008/9 for elective procedures, and some signs that equity might have improved slightly as inpatient admission rates rose slightly faster in low-income areas than elsewhere (Cookson *et al* 2010b). These findings are also consistent with another recent study using routine patient-level data, which showed that socio-economic equity in colorectal, breast and lung cancer procedures changed little between 1999 and 2006 (Raine *et al* 2010).

Similarly, another longitudinal study using routine NHS hospital data looked at socio-economic variation in NHS hospital waiting times for hip replacement, knee replacement and cataract surgery between 1999 and 2007, a timespan that covered both the period when New Labour drove reform exclusively through targets and top-down performance management, and later when it had reintroduced the quasi-market alongside its other policy instruments (Cooper *et al* 2009). Its authors found that the deprivation gradient of waiting (ie, people in more deprived areas tending to wait slightly longer than those in less deprived areas) at the beginning of the period had disappeared and might even have slightly reversed by 2002 (the heyday of 'targets and terror'), and that little had changed thereafter when the market was reintroduced.

One explanation for the findings of Cookson *et al* (2010) and those of Cooper *et al* (2009) is that the pressure to meet waiting-time targets that began before the market reforms and persisted throughout the reform period was having a greater effect than any consequence of private-sector entry and/or competition. This is consistent with the findings of local case-study research on the impact of the reform mechanisms by Powell *et al* (2011), and with the Civitas analysis that the NHS market operated in only isolated pockets and for only a small number of services (Brereton and Gubb 2010). It is therefore possible that the lack of any rise in inequity associated with market competition in the 1990s and 2000s occurred not because the NHS market was designed to prevent or even reduce inequity, but because it was operating only weakly. If true, such an inference has major implications for the future impact of the market given that the coalition government aims to implement a fully-functioning market in the English NHS (*see* Chapter 10).

Overall verdict on the impact of the market reform

Despite the strong overlay of previous hierarchical policies driven by targets and performance management, New Labour's market appeared to contain stronger incentives for quality and efficiency than did its 1990s' predecessor – as exemplified in the system of PbR with its encouragement to provider competition for patients, but without any obvious incentives to reduce quality – and these effects seem to have gathered pace during the period up to 2010, as the more recent studies reviewed here tended to find more positive results than did earlier assessments (Audit Commission and Healthcare Commission 2008), suggesting that it took a number of years for the changes announced in 2002/3 to begin to have their impact.

It is interesting in this regard to note the findings of parallel studies of organisational culture in the NHS, which report an increase in the proportion of NHS trusts displaying a so-called entrepreneurial organisational culture and a decrease in the proportion displaying a tribal, inward-looking culture over the same period (Mannion *et al* 2009), suggesting that market thinking and behaviour became more deep-rooted in the 2000s than in the 1990s. This is likely to continue since the coalition government of May 2010 is committed to accelerating and deepening the extent to which the English NHS sees itself and behaves as a regulated provider market.

Quality of, and gaps in, the evidence

During the early 1990s, Kenneth Clarke, as Conservative Secretary of State for Health, resisted pressure both to pilot his radical internal market proposals and then to commission evaluation of the impact of the subsequent legislation. Instead, it was left to The King's Fund to commission its own independent research (Robinson and Le Grand 1994). By contrast, it is to the credit of the New Labour government that, in 2006, it commissioned a programme of evaluation of its post-2002/3 reforms, which has formed the backbone of this book. The studies in the Health Reform Evaluation Programme covered all the reform mechanisms, with the exception of primary research on the impact of the new quality and financial regulators, and, to a lesser extent, attempted to study the interaction of the mechanisms. However, as is almost always the case with major public policy reform, both proponents and detractors would like more, and more definitive, evidence on the impact and the causal pathways leading to those impacts.

Despite the fact that the Department of Health was willing to fund a substantial programme of independent research on the impact of the reforms, the number of studies on the changes is still very small in relation to the extent of change in the period and the potential benefits and risks of the reforms. For example, there is only a handful of quantitative studies of the NHS hospital market as a whole over time (Farrar *et al* 2009; Cooper *et al* 2010, 2011; Gaynor *et al* 2011) compared with the evidence available in countries such as the United States. It is to be hoped that the longitudinal evidence on the impact of market-related policies on a tax-financed system will accumulate rapidly in future as the coalition government continues with market-based reforms.

On the other hand, calls for more, and more definitive, research tend to overlook or downplay the many challenges encountered in evaluating major health care system change, all of which have affected the evidence presented in this book. The main difficulties were:

- dealing with the fact that the reforms were simultaneously introduced across the whole of England rather than being piloted or phased in particular regions

- determining when the market reforms were fully operational and, therefore, should be evaluated for their impact, given that they were introduced in stages over time and that some elements such as the quality regulator were introduced before the market itself had been reconstituted; the entire package of market-related changes was not fully operational until early 2006 at the earliest, leaving a relatively short period of time to fund and undertake studies, and observe changes

- separating out the impact of the different elements in the reforms, particularly the independent contribution of individual patient choice of place of elective treatment versus the staged implementation of PbR, and the impact of changes to commissioning versus policies directly targeting the providers of care

- deciding how to attribute the changes observed to particular policies, and to the market reforms in particular, given the lags between the introduction of the changes and their possible effects, the instability in institutional settings, especially commissioning organisations and regulatory bodies (with constant reorganisation of PCTs and the quality regulator during the 2000s), and the contemporaneous impact of other unrelated policy changes, such as the introduction of a new GP contract involving payment for quality, national service frameworks and increases in funding

- measuring (and trading off) the different impacts of the reforms when many of the studies described in the rest of the book are reliant on national-level administrative datasets; although there is evidence that these datasets have been improving in the recent past, they frequently lack crucial information, for example, there are few proxy measures of care quality and outcomes in the English hospital episode statistics (eg, in-hospital mortality, wound infection rates), and efficiency (eg, day-case rates and lengths of stay)

■ how to interpret the 'black-box' findings of national-level quantitative studies based on administrative data using qualitative case studies based largely on participants' perceptions.

Despite the many difficulties of reaching definitive conclusions on the reforms, their design and implementation held a number of advantages for evaluation that should not be ignored, especially those relating to the:

■ phased implementation of the changes over time (eg, the gradual extension of PbR to different specialties in particular)

■ the natural experiment of market changes in England, but not in Scotland (eg, there were no comparable market changes such as PbR in Scotland).

Both these characteristics of the implementation of the market reforms were able to be used positively in the evaluation studies in the Health Reform Evaluation Programme. Nonetheless, there are ways in which future evaluation programmes might be improved. In particular, more adaptive models of research could be encouraged that could respond flexibly to a changing policy context. There is much that should be done to speed up access to administrative data and research governance permissions to allow researchers to interview staff and patients. There may also be scope to undertake interviews with policy-makers and implementers in real time to avoid *post hoc* rationalisation of the effects of reforms. Finally, there is an increasing need to undertake studies that explicitly relate large-scale, quantitative analyses using administrative datasets to more in-depth investigations designed to help explain the quantitative findings.

Challenges apparent by 2010 and requiring further development of market policies

Based on the situation of the English NHS at the end of New Labour's time in office, Brereton and Gubb (2010) from free-market think-tank Civitas concluded that there were still too many barriers to the operation of a market for NHS services rather than there being a fatal flaw in the concept. Indeed, arguably, there had been a slowing down and even a partial reversal of pro-market policy in the NHS at the end of the period, when Andy Burnham was Secretary of State. The distortions they highlighted were:

■ power imbalances between PCT commissioners and providers, particularly acute NHS trusts

- the lack of a level playing field between NHS and non-NHS providers to the detriment of the latter (Burnham had weakened the government's commitment to any willing provider being able to offer its services to treat NHS patients as long as it could meet NHS quality standards and the PbR tariff price)

- continuing perverse incentives under PbR to admit patients who would be better off out of hospital.

They further argued that there were still too many restrictions on non-NHS providers entering the NHS market, and a lack of skills relevant to working in a market among both commissioners and providers. The implication of their analysis was that freeing up the NHS market further would alter the balance of benefits and costs of the market changes in favour of the former. Arguably, this is exactly what the coalition government's proposed reforms are designed to do (Department of Health 2010). Broadening the scope and degree of provider competition for NHS services raises many challenges, not least a major improvement in the information on the quality of care offered by different providers so that patients and commissioners can make better-informed choices, and the ability to develop services for people with complex chronic conditions requiring co-ordination between providers rather than competition. These and other challenges are discussed in the final chapter in the light of the evidence on the implementation and impact of New Labour's market reforms assembled in the previous chapters.

10 Lessons for future health care reforms in England

Anna Dixon and Nicholas Mays

As the National Health Service (NHS) enters a new decade in 2011, it faces one of its toughest financial periods ever. Despite NHS spending being protected from cuts, the equivalent of 0 per cent real growth (or thereabouts after adjusting for inflation) will mean the need to make efficiency savings of around 4 per cent per annum in order to close the estimated £20 billion productivity gap (Appleby *et al* 2009). This is in stark contrast to the 5–6 per cent per annum growth in real terms enjoyed by the NHS during the period of the Labour government.

The general election in May 2010 resulted in the formation of the first coalition government for more than half a century, comprising the Conservative Party and the Liberal Democrats. Before the election, both parties had set out proposals to reform the NHS in their manifestos. A broad statement of the reforms the coalition was intending to implement was then presented in its programme for government. Despite a promise to 'stop the top-down reorganisations of the NHS that have got in the way of patient care' (Her Majesty's Government 2010, p 24), the coalition government proposed a set of wide-reaching and radical reforms to the NHS (Department of Health 2010).

The stated aims are to reduce bureaucracy and empower clinicians to make commissioning decisions on behalf of patients, and to give patients greater choice and access to information. The overall aim appears to be to transform the NHS into a system in which there is greater financial transparency and services are shaped by rules-based market regulation.

The key proposals are to:

- give responsibility for commissioning the majority of health care services to general practitioners (GPs) working in consortia
- create an independent NHS Commissioning Board to allocate resources to and oversee GP consortia
- abolish strategic health authorities (SHAs) and primary care trusts (PCTs)
- introduce an outcomes framework for holding a new NHS Commissioning Board to account instead of targets and performance management

- transfer public health responsibilities to local authorities, and create local health and wellbeing boards to promote integration of health and social care

- set up local HealthWatch groups funded by local government to replace local involvement networks to help the public and patients influence local services, with a national HealthWatch body within the Care Quality Commission (CQC)

- give greater freedoms to publicly owned providers of health care, and an aspiration to see more social enterprises serving NHS patients

- extend individual patient choice of hospital to include specific specialists or clinical teams

- create an economic regulator that will set prices, promote competition and ensure continuity of essential services.

Following consultation on these proposals (Department of Health 2010b, 2010c) and the government's response to the consultation, the government introduced the Health and Social Care Bill to parliament in January 2011. The Bill made clear the intention that choice and competition should play a much greater role in driving and shaping services in future. In April – in an unprecedented move – the government 'paused' the legislative process in order to conduct a listening exercise. This was in part a response to growing opposition from stakeholders and disquiet within the NHS and among the Liberal Democrats about how far and how fast the government was pushing through these competition reforms. The NHS Future Forum was set up and asked to make recommendations about how the Bill should be changed (NHS Future Forum 2011).

In response to the Future Forum the government has introduced a series of amendments to the Health and Social Care Bill (Department of Health 2011a, 2011b). Clinical commissioning groups will be responsible for commissioning care. These will still largely be GP-led but the governing bodies will include other health professionals and patient and public representatives. The economic regulator will tackle anti-competitive behaviour where this is not in the interests of patients rather than specifically promote competition. There are also new duties on various bodies to enable services to be provided in an integrated way.

In intellectual terms, these proposals do represent, to a great extent, an evolution of the NHS market, and do share some similarities with New Labour's market reforms. However, they also involve large-scale organisational disruption. Although it is clear that NHS services do need to change radically in order to deliver the required savings, there is evidence that system-wide structural and organisational reforms (so-called big bang changes) take time to produce savings and, in the short term, are likely to increase costs and distract attention from improving productivity (NHS Confederation 2010; Walshe 2010).

The detail of the proposals is still to be finalised, but the general direction – to create a mixed economy of providers of care, with greater choice for patients, devolved financial responsibility to clinicians, and more transparent reimbursement mechanisms, underpinned by regulation – is unlikely to be dramatically different. It is hoped that this review of the evidence of the impact and experience of implementing the market reforms introduced by the last Labour government can provide some insights to ensure that both the design and execution of the latest set of competition reforms will be informed by evidence as well as shaped by politics. The lessons from this book will also serve a more general purpose: to inform any future policy-makers seeking to reform the health system about the challenges of success.

In this chapter, for each of the key aspects of reform covered in this book we compare the reforms being proposed by the coalition government with the reforms analysed in this book, and reflect on the evidence presented to suggest what might happen and what needs to happen in order to ensure that the reforms deliver benefits and minimise harm and disruption.

Diversity of providers

The coalition government proposes to complete the process begun by New Labour to give all publicly owned providers greater autonomy. Although the Labour government made similar commitments, deadlines were revised and repeatedly missed. The evidence suggests that a lack of robust financial planning and governance was often the cause of trusts failing to gain authorisation. The more challenging financial environment is likely to mean that trusts can no longer rely on expanding market share to ensure their financial viability and underpin business plans. This suggests that, for some trusts, the transition to foundation trust status is likely to prove difficult if not impossible. The government is establishing a special health authority to take over responsibility from SHAs to prepare trusts for foundation trust authorisation and to find other solutions for trusts that will not be able to gain it (such as mergers or closures or possibly franchised management).

Given that foundation trusts were higher performing trusts in the first place, it is difficult to establish whether foundation trust status per se has resulted in improvements in quality, and there is very little research on the impact of foundation trust status on quality of care (*see* Chapter 2). Evidence suggests that the process of authorisation itself could result in improvements. This has implications not only for how the authorisation of the remaining foundation trusts is handled, but also for whether the authorisation process for clinical commissioning groups can be structured in such a way that it results in improvements in commissioning over time.

The policy objectives of giving foundation trusts greater freedoms remain the same: to enable them to innovate and be more responsive. In future, foundation trusts will have greater freedoms and there will be less direct oversight as Monitor's role changes. Instead, there will be a stronger role for governors and members in holding the organisation to account. Evidence suggests that foundation trusts have not made extensive use of their existing freedoms, such as flexibility on pay and conditions. Most have been risk-averse and not sought to invest or borrow. By making the most of first-mover advantage and the freedom to take decisions more swiftly, foundation trusts have been able to expand more quickly than have other providers. Some foundation trusts have generated significant surpluses, which they are able to use to invest in new services or expand existing services. In some cases, this has been at the expense of co-operative and collaborative relationships with other providers and commissioners, although the evidence of whether foundation trusts were more competitive than non-foundation trusts is mixed (*see* Chapter 4). Finally, governors have been relatively weak and not able to play an effective role in the governance of foundation trusts.

The tighter funding environment means that new foundation trusts are unlikely to be able to generate surpluses and might therefore have more appetite to borrow than existing foundation trusts have done, although borrowing in the current financial climate may be difficult and expensive. If foundation trusts use their freedoms actively to compete and expand, this may well be at the expense of other providers and other parts of the system. There is a real danger that institutions will put their own organisational survival above the interests of the system as a whole.

In the past, commissioners found it difficult to challenge the dominance of acute foundation trusts, and policies to shift more care out of hospital have largely failed to find traction. The scale of productivity improvements now required means that organisations will need to look across care pathways and services – not just within organisations – to reduce waste and eliminate inefficiencies (Appleby *et al* 2010). It is not clear who would lead such processes under the new system. Mergers and acquisitions of trusts by foundation trusts could be positive if they result in improvements in services, but there is also a risk that they will reduce access and savings will fail to be realised (Palmer 2011). The only means of ensuring that foundation trusts operate in the public interest in future will be through their accountability to members. This places a great deal of faith in structures that have, to date, failed to prove their effectiveness.

As part of its wider proposals on public service reform, the government wants up to 25 per cent of all public procurement contracts (by value) to be awarded to small and medium-sized enterprises (Her Majesty's Government 2010, p 10), and is promoting the mutualisation of public services. The government has recently published guidance suggesting that NHS staff would have the 'right to provide' by becoming employee-owned social enterprises (Department of Health 2011c). Although in the past this was an aspiration for community health service providers, few made the transition to social enterprise status. Many of the reasons why this organisational form was not an attractive option, such as risks to NHS pension entitlements, are also likely to be the case for other NHS staff in future (Addicott 2011).

The government is also interested in the private and voluntary sector playing a much bigger role as providers of NHS-funded services. The attitudes of commissioners and their approach to commissioning will be extremely important. Tendering processes may open up opportunities to new providers, but it will depend on what is being tendered and whether the barriers to entry are high. 'Any qualified provider' might, in theory, facilitate the emergence of new entrants, but the private sector, and to some degree the voluntary sector, will want scale, certainty and scope. Independent-sector treatment centres (ISTCs) were able to enter the market partly because they were offered certainty and a premium to cover the additional costs of setting up a new business. No such offer is on the table for new entrants in future, indeed the government has ruled out giving any unfair advantage to a particular sector.

The period examined in this book was one of growth, both in funding and activity volumes, which meant that new entrants and the growth in provision by the private sector did not destabilise NHS providers. However, the colder economic climate means that a greater diversity of providers and new entrants in the future would necessarily take activity away from incumbent providers.

Financial pressures over the past few years have meant that trusts that have not yet achieved foundation trust status, and even some that have, will struggle to remain viable if they lose activity and funding is removed at full tariff without the ability to downsize (ie, reduce fixed costs). Commissioners may find themselves subsidising local designated (ie, essential) services because other, more lucrative or interdependent, clinical activities have closed as a result of patients and referrers having taken their business elsewhere.

One of the challenges of comparing the quality of care and performance of public and private providers under New Labour was the lack of standardised data available for such a purpose. It is vital that throughout the regulatory and contracting process, the information and data requirements are the same for all NHS-funded care to ensure that, for the purposes of both commissioning and evaluation, these comparisons can be made robustly in future, taking differences in casemix into account.

The ownership status of providers appears not to have a differential effect on quality of care, but there remains a danger of fragmentation when providers are competing for patients. The question remains as to whether the system can encourage new partnerships and joint ventures between public and private organisations. Rather than collaboration (or collusion), there need to be more overt partnerships, in which the risks and rewards to each party are more clearly defined, and the financial risk and gain-sharing arrangements are clear.

The emphasis of policy to date has been on creating a mixed market of providers. If the objective is greater responsiveness and more innovation, then a true diversity of provision, meaning different models of care, is needed. In future, there are likely to be new forms of primary care, such as federations and integrated care organisations. Academic health science centres may develop further into larger integrated delivery systems, and, depending on future contract negotiations, chambers and multispecialty groups of clinicians may evolve as separate operating companies.

Much will depend on how the other parts of the system develop, for example, the attitude of commissioners and their approach to commissioning, the structure and basis of tariffs and resource allocation, and the regulatory framework. Providers will change and adapt to meet the changing incentives and requirements created by the system within the constraints set by regulation.

Overall, the extent and impact of provider-side reforms at the end of the period of the Labour government was limited. The proportion of NHS-funded activity in the private sector remained small, with entry limited largely to ISTCs, which benefitted from secure contract terms. Almost half of trusts had not become foundation trusts, and those that had achieved authorisation were slow to use their freedoms. Finally, few community health service providers had opted to become social enterprises, with many preferring to stay under NHS ownership.

Looking ahead to a tighter funding environment, the coalition government's ambition to see a greater plurality of provision, the mutualisation of public services, and the transfer of all publicly owned providers to foundation trust status seems unlikely to be realised. Unless barriers to entry are reduced, incumbent providers are displaced or allowed to fail, and issues such as the transferability of public-sector pensions and terms and conditions are tackled, NHS-funded care is likely to continue to be largely provided by publicly owned providers. The evidence on differences in performance on cost and quality between public and private providers also remains largely unknown, so the case for plurality is hard to make definitively.

Commissioning

PCTs are to be abolished and commissioning responsibilities devolved to clinical commissioning groups. Some specialist commissioning will be undertaken directly by the NHS Commissioning Board, which will also authorise local commissioning groups and hold national contracts for primary medical services. The government's proposals build on previous initiatives – GP fundholding and total purchasing pilots in the 1990s, and practice-based commissioning (PBC) in the past decade, which enabled groups of GPs to take on responsibility for commissioning some services on a voluntary basis. However, they go much further by making membership compulsory and giving full budgetary responsibility for commissioning the majority of services.

Evidence suggests there is no one right level at which commissioning of all health services should take place (Smith *et al* 2004). This may explain why there have been numerous reorganisations of commissioning, and why both devolved structures (PBC) and collaborative structures (clusters) have been created. Repeated reorganisations seriously undermined the ability of commissioners to mature and operate effectively as commissioners. It is therefore unfortunate that in an effort to improve commissioning, the government has embarked on another major restructuring. Although these changes could address the lack of clinical engagement in commissioning – a key weakness of PCTs – there is a high chance that, over time, they will come to look very similar to PCTs but with GPs and other clinicians more actively involved (at least for a while) in the governance of the groups.

PBC sought to try to devolve clinical and financial responsibility to GPs, but the lack of hard budgets limited the incentives for better use of resources, and GPs felt frustrated by the probity requirements placed on them by PCTs to produce business cases to justify service changes affecting primary care. The vast majority of service changes associated with PBC were focused on the provision of primary care and community-based services rather than shaping secondary care. Although the incentives on member practices to live within a budget are likely to be greater, concerns have been expressed that, if too strong, GPs may make decisions based on financial grounds rather than in the best interests of individual patients.

The reality is that all decisions necessarily combine a financial and clinical component. By having clearer budgetary responsibility, the financial considerations are more explicit. There is a danger that, for most ordinary GPs, clinical commissioning groups will feel remote, and few will have either the interest or skills to engage in commissioning more complex secondary and tertiary services. As providers, GPs wanting to provide extended or new services in the community will most likely have to tender for these contracts. This may feel as bureaucratic as the business-case process they were forced to go through under PBC. Although there is some evidence that GPs may feel more accountable to their peers than they did to PCTs, particularly for elements such as referrals and prescribing, there is a danger that those leading the consortia will have little authority or leverage to tackle practices that consistently underperform.

Much of the evidence has focused on the structures of commissioning rather than evaluating how effectively commissioners actually commission or the adequacy of the tools and approaches available to them to carry out their key functions. Other than information from CQC assessments and world class commissioning assurance, there is almost no academic research about the effectiveness of commissioning under New Labour (*see* Chapter 3). The Department of Health provided PCTs with national contracts, but these were organisational contracts (eg, for acute providers, mental health trusts and community services) that focused on volumes of service. PCTs also had to use a fixed tariff for a range of services (*see* below) as the basis of payment, and did not use what little flexibility they had to bundle or unbundle these defined episodes of care. Much of the contracting process was focused on validating the invoices; there was much less attention paid to monitoring the quality of services delivered. PCTs that were interested in redesigning services had to undertake this locally – drawing up the service specification or care pathway (often involving clinicians in this process) and then contracting for bits of the service or care pathway with different organisations using different payments. If the new local commissioning bodies attempt this they will not be able to live within their management allowance, and the duplication of activity could be worse than it is currently.

What is really needed is a renewed understanding of what commissioning is and how to do it – an approach that promotes integration of services, particularly for people with multiple conditions and complex care needs. This could be led by the NHS Commissioning Board, which, if it chose to, could provide more sophisticated and specialist support to local commissioners than the Department of Health was able to do.

The current national standard contracts do not provide local commissioners with the tools to do the job effectively, and the design of tariffs and price-setting limits the ability of local commissioners to incentivise integration and innovation. Commissioners need to focus on the key functions of:

- assessing need
- setting priorities
- allocating resources
- contracting for services
- measuring performance against those contracts.

To do this, they need to set some outcomes (together with some intermediate measures that allow performance to be tracked and monitored over shorter time periods), and to have methods of reimbursement that transfer risk and the incentives for efficiency and quality to providers. Transactional contracting requires its own bureaucracy to manage and police it, and the information asymmetries that exist are difficult for commissioners to overcome. There is a need for commissioners to move to longer-term relational contracts so as to allow more mature commissioner–provider relationships to evolve. Service redesign then becomes a provider-led activity in response to the priorities, outcomes and resource decisions taken by commissioners.

The key tests will be whether clinical commissioning groups are any more effective in creating an environment in which there are opportunities for providers to develop new models of care and which encourage providers to form partnerships and joint ventures to take on greater financial risk and responsibility. The tighter financial context means commissioners will again have to face more difficult decisions about which services to commission. The spectre of rationing and priority-setting looms large, and commissioners will have to use more sophisticated approaches to engage the public, patients and clinicians in these difficult choices.

An alternative policy direction would be to reverse the trends of recent years and to allow greater commissioner–provider integration. As others have demonstrated (Smith *et al* 2010), the purity of commissioning has rarely existed in practice, and providers play a significant role in the commissioning process because of their generally superior knowledge of the services in question. The original intentions behind devolving budgets to groups of GPs was to allow them to take so-called make or buy decisions. There is still a lack of clarity about whether public procurement rules and European Union (EU) competition law will allow this, and it will obviously require conflicts of interest to be handled in a transparent way (Ham 2011).

The evidence on commissioning, both from the period covered here (*see* Chapter 3) and also internationally, suggests it is very challenging to do commissioning well. PCTs and PBC were beginning to develop skills towards the end of the period. There is a risk that the current restructuring of PCTs will result in a loss of expertise, setting commissioning back yet again, and that the development of new clinical commissioning groups will take a long time.

Evidence suggests that devolving financial responsibility to clinicians, can bring benefits, but also that there is a need to commission at different levels. This suggests the focus should be less on getting the right structures and governance arrangements, and more on what and how services are commissioned.

Choice

The government is committed to extending patient choice of provider, but has also put a renewed focus on involving patients more in decisions about their care and treatment (Department of Health 2010d). Patient choice is to be extended in primary care with the abolition of practice boundaries, and the government has indicated that it wishes to extend free choice (under an any willing provider arrangement similar to that in place currently for choice at point of referral to secondary care) to other services, including community health services. The government is committed to publishing more information on performance and quality of care, including feedback from other patients and patient-reported outcomes.

Evidence suggests that although few patients actually exercise choice and go to an alternative to their local NHS provider, they still value having a choice and appear to use it to avoid attending a local hospital where they have had a bad experience on a previous occasion. Available evidence is largely based on choice at the point of referral for a specialist consultation, and it is not clear how generalisable the findings are to other types of choice. For example, in general practice, patients with a minor problem may value convenience and speed of access, whereas patients with ongoing medical conditions may value a trusted relationship and be loyal to their registered practice and usual doctor. If, as is proposed, choice is at the point of registration rather than the point of access, then patients are unlikely to switch frequently.

There is some evidence to suggest that patients may value choice of provider at a later stage in the care pathway, when the decision is taken to undergo more invasive or high-risk treatment, and this is also a stage when patients could benefit from more support to consider the risks and benefits as part of shared decision-making. If more direct access diagnostics are available in primary care in future, this might change the decision point.

Making more information available will not necessarily mean that it is used to inform decisions. Neither patients nor GPs currently make use of the published data that are available to inform their decisions, relying instead on personal knowledge and experience. Measures of clinical quality are also difficult to understand and interpret, and, although there are ways of presenting information that can help (Boyce *et al* 2010), patients are likely to pay more attention to other patients' feedback.

There is at least some evidence to suggest that GPs believe choice of treatment or care plan is more important than where that treatment or care is accessed. It is important that any information strategy recognises this, and invests in reliable information and decision support about treatment and care options as well as quality information about different providers. There is a possibility that, as more people become aware of quality differences between providers, they might be willing to travel further to access better care, particularly if GPs advise patients to do so on clinical grounds. However, clinically led reconfigurations of services may result in some more specialist services being concentrated in fewer centres, thus reducing the number of choices and meaning patients have to travel further to access services.

In general, the evidence suggests that GPs are reluctant to offer patients choice routinely, and have their own views about when and for whom it is relevant. GPs are also powerful agents – when they do offer choice, patients rely on their recommendations to inform their own decisions. There is a risk that, with greater budgetary accountability, there will be increasing pressure on GPs not to refer. If patients perceive GPs to have such conflicts of interest, they may no longer trust them to be independent advisers to support their choice.

GPs are likely to continue to play an important role in supporting patients to make decisions about where to go and, increasingly, in making choices about their lifestyle, care plans and treatment choices (Coulter and Collins 2011). There is a need to be clear about when it is appropriate to offer patients a choice and what sort of choices, what and how many options to make available, and how best to support the decision with advice and information.

Evidence suggests that patients and GPs are generally loyal to local providers. This, combined with the reluctance of GPs to support choice, suggests that the system should not rely on patient choice alone to drive competition in future. Furthermore, despite the availability of increasing amounts of information on the quality of providers, this does not appear to drive quality competition through choice, but rather through reputational effects and peer competition.

Pricing and reimbursement

In future, price-setting through Payment by Results (PbR) is to be undertaken jointly by Monitor and the NHS Commissioning Board. The intention appears to be to move away from an activity-based payment system calculated using average costs, to one that rewards quality and promotes efficiency using more detailed patient-level costing data from a sample of providers. This builds on developments already implemented, such as best practice tariffs, as well as schemes such as commissioning for quality and innovation (CQUIN) and the decision not to pay for a list of so-called never events, or for readmissions within 30 days of hospital discharge.

Evidence suggests that the use of fixed prices has led to improvements in outcomes because it promotes quality competition. In addition to setting fixed prices, the Bill originally allowed Monitor to specify a maximum tariff, thus enabling the introduction of competition on price as well as quality. Experience from the United States (Gaynor 2004) and from the internal market in the NHS in the early 1990s (Propper *et al* 2008a) suggests that hospital price competition may reduce quality as providers seek to lower costs. It could also increase transaction costs, with commissioners and providers spending significant amounts of time negotiating prices. Price competition has now been ruled out, at least where services are to be offered under an any qualified provider arrangement. Where services are tendered, commissioners will be able to use their purchasing power to get value for money.

Despite commitments to roll out PbR to other services including mental health, implementation has been slow. It is important that policy-makers recognise that some types of care are not suited to activity-based payments and may need to be purchased under block contracts (eg, intensive care beds, for which the key issue is availability rather than throughput) or other reimbursement models.

The current trend has been to unbundle in order to be able to pay a different provider for a different part of the care pathway in a different setting. This places an incredible burden on the commissioner and generates high transaction costs. Tariffs in future can comprise one or more services, suggesting a move away from narrowly defined tariffs based on episodes of care, to more aggregated or bundled payments. It is not clear to what extent national bodies or indeed local commissioners could commission a year of care for a diabetic patient, or go further and contract with a lead provider or a consortium of organisations to take on a risk-based capitation payment in return for meeting a wide range of care needs for a defined population.

In a more market-based system, price-setting is a very important policy instrument with potentially powerful effects. The main concerns with fixed prices were that PbR might lead to risk selection (ie, providers would try to shun patients who were poor with more complex needs), upcoding, and quality skimping. There appears to be little evidence of these behaviours having been widespread. Indeed, the evidence points to benefits in terms of improved technical efficiency and no deterioration in quality. Monitor will need to continue to scrutinise the impact of its pricing to ensure that it does not provide incentives for these undesirable behaviours.

There was little evidence of inequities arising as a result of pricing. It is not possible to observe whether patient selection did not occur because there were no incentives to do so (ie, the casemix adjustment was adequate or the overall financial environment was sufficiently benign), or because the decision-making by clinicians did not allow this to occur in practice. On the whole, the private sector treated a less complex casemix, which is partly explained by an overt selection process for ISTCs due to their lack of intensive care facilities. The less complex casemix in the private sector is not, in itself, a problem, but rather depends on whether prices are adequately adjusted to ensure that these providers do not make a windfall profit at the expense of public providers whose case severity and acuity is higher.

There was little evidence of extensive upcoding, but some evidence that the quality of coding improved. It is not clear whether this was because the incentives to do so did not penetrate to the people responsible for coding, or whether the threat of action for such behaviour was sufficient. What is clear is that there are considerable administrative costs associated with monitoring providers' coding and billing through utilisation review and resolving billing disputes. A real test of the new system will be whether such transaction costs can be reduced, either through bundling payments and transferring risk to the providers, or because, clinicians will be more aware of the appropriateness of treatment and therefore more able to challenge overuse than were administrators in PCTs.

Despite a belief, particularly among commissioners, that PbR has resulted in increased activity in hospitals, the evidence suggests that other factors probably account for a good part of the rise in hospital activity in England, such as waiting-time targets for elective care and greater acuity of problems in older people for emergency admissions. The tariff means that hospitals were paid for the increased levels of activity, but it did not necessarily act as an incentive to increase activity, particularly among providers whose costs were generally above tariff levels. If the imperative now is to reduce hospital activity, then the challenge is for commissioners, working with providers, to ensure that referrals for treatment are appropriate, and that care is in place to support frail older people and those with complex needs so as to prevent admission. There has been a tendency among commissioners to blame PbR and foundation trusts for the growth in hospital activity, despite the lack of strong evidence.

Currently, data to support more sophisticated and accurate price-setting are not available across the public and private sectors, although providing such data is likely to become a condition of being licensed by Monitor in future. Price-setting is not simply a technical exercise, but requires difficult trade-offs to be made between quality, efficiency, access and affordability. How these issues will be reconciled among the NHS Commissioning Board, the CQC and Monitor is not entirely clear. Monitor will need to model the impacts of pricing carefully – if prices are set too low, quality might be driven down or providers might withdraw services; if the price is set too high, commissioners could be bankrupted.

It appears that PbR rewarded hospitals that increased their activity in response to the targets to reduce waiting times, but did not itself drive activity. Access as a problem has largely been resolved, although the current fiscal tightening could see it reappear as an issue. The main challenge facing the health system in the future is the management of chronic illness. The objectives of the pricing and reimbursement arrangements need to adjust to this, too. The adverse impacts and gaming were not as bad as feared, but these need to be carefully monitored under any future system.

Regulation and competition

From April 2012, Monitor will become an economic regulator for health and social care. The Health and Social Care Bill gives Monitor wide-ranging powers to impose licence conditions to prevent anti-competitive behaviour, to apply sanctions to enforce competition law, and to refer malfunctioning markets to the Competition Commission. The proposals introduce a clearer system of special administration to deal with providers that fail financially, that is, become insolvent.

The policies discussed above to encourage a greater diversity of providers, to extend patient choice and to allow any willing provider to offer specific NHS-funded services, might suggest that competition will increase. However, there is likely to be considerable consolidation of providers over the next few years, particularly in acute hospital care, as a result of the financial context, clearer rules on provider failure, the deadline for foundation trusts, the clinical and financial case for reconfiguration, and better management of patients outside hospital. This could reduce spatial competition, increase the concentration of markets in specialist services and, where mergers take place, reduce the number of competitors.

The type of competition promoted under the New Labour reforms was mainly between hospitals for individual patients. In some areas and to a more limited extent, there was also competition for contracts for out-of-hospital services. Concerns about the impact of competition, particularly that it will result in greater fragmentation, assume that competition will be largely *in* the market, between single providers for discrete items of service (eg, hip surgery). There is nothing inherent in competition or the rules that are used to enforce it that mean competition needs to be of this sort. For example, the unit of competition does not need to be a hospital, but could be between integrated delivery systems or networks of providers. It could be for a whole package of care rather than a single part of the care pathway, and tendering does not need to result in selective contracting with a single provider. There is probably a need to combine both approaches to competition. For example, through tendering and procurement a commissioner could require providers to compete to be 'in network', and then encourage competition between providers in the network for patients, thus allowing for both price competition (via tendering) and quality competition (via choice). An integrated care provider could be prevented from restricting choice, and might be required to allow patients to deviate from the pathway or package of care and go outside the integrated care organisation. If this is the case, integrated providers would have to win the loyalty of patients for them to remain within the network.

There has also been some confusion about whether the government's reforms will open up the health care system to EU competition law more than it is currently. By bringing the NHS under the aegis of the Office of Fair Trading, it is clear that EU competition law will now apply. This covers issues such as state aid, mergers, cartels and preventing monopoly. However, EU competition law applies only to so-called undertakings. There is no legal clarity on the definition of an undertaking, but foundation trusts are likely to be regarded as such, particularly as they are allowed to compete for private patients. The lifting of the private patient cap will make this more likely. Case law has established that purchasers of public services that operate with social objectives are not considered to be undertakings, so neither PCTs nor other statutory commissioning bodies are likely to be subject to competition law, although, again, this is not clear. EU procurement principles already apply to PCTs, and would require commissioners to be compliant in future. There is no requirement under these principles to tender services. A public body could decide to provide the services itself, but if it decides to tender, then it must comply with the principles. However, the Department of Health's own procurement guidance (Department of Health 2010f) does go further in this regard, and might limit the ability of clinical commissioning groups to take make or buy decisions.

It is likely that there will continue to be a mix of competition in the market (ie, for patients) and for the market (ie, for contracts). In what circumstances these two modes are used, and for which types of services, will be key in determining the nature and impact of competition. Recent policy discussions have clarified that this will be a matter for commissioners (House of Commons Health Select Committee 2011). It must be remembered, however, that the evidence on choice suggests that patients (and GPs) are loyal to local providers, and this so-called stickiness could limit the extent of competition in the market. Although some benefits have been demonstrated in terms of quality, more research is needed to understand where and how to apply competition so that it delivers benefits.

No new changes are proposed to the CQC, which will continue to register service providers across health and social care and the public and private sectors. The CQC has had to downsize and rationalise its activities. The government planned to continue to adopt a risk-based approach to inspection, relying on self-assessments and CQC's own risk profiling using routine data. However, as this book was going to press, CQC announced revised plans to include unannounced site visits, suggesting a shift away from 'light touch' regulation. The evidence suggests that without regular inspections it is difficult for regulators to be assured that quality standards are being met – they need to see and hear things on the ground (*see* Chapter 7). Light touch regulation also relies on the ability of the governance boards of providers to engage with issues of clinical quality and safety, and on strong internal governance. The CQC has stronger sanctioning powers than did its predecessors, and is likely to have to intervene more often in future.

The application of competition rules to the NHS by the Co-operation and Competition Panel was introduced relatively late in the process of reforms, and the cases referred to it have not been reviewed here. There is little evidence so far on which to judge the proposals for an economic regulator. More relevant perhaps is the evidence from the utilities' regulators and from countries such as The Netherlands where there is a health sector-specific competition authority. The system of regulation developed during this period focused on licensing all providers on quality and safety grounds. The evidence presented here suggests that there may need to be more investment in the process of monitoring and inspection if the regulator is going to be able to detect failures and breaches in standards.

Building blocks of a market-based health system

This chapter has reflected on the evidence on the impact of market reforms under Labour (summarised in Chapter 9), and the implications for the continuation and strengthening of the market in health care as proposed by the coalition government. These point to a number of key points that need attention if the system is to deliver, and a number of areas where further research is needed:

- ensuring robust governance of foundation trusts and rectifying the lack of meaningful local public accountability; further research is needed into the effectiveness of their boards and what the key factors are that determine their ability to monitor and assure both clinical and financial performance

- improving the routinely available data and indicators of the quality of care offered by different providers so that patients and commissioners are able to make better-informed choices, and so that competition is genuinely on the basis of quality; this would also allow meaningful comparisons of the costs and quality of services delivered by different types of provider organisations (eg, foundation trusts versus independent sector hospitals, social enterprises versus professional partnerships versus community foundation trusts in the delivery of community health services, etc)

- developing more sophisticated approaches to commissioning and providing support to commissioners so that they operate more effectively; more evidence about how to commission for outcomes, use of risk-based payments and risk-sharing agreements, and different contracting models that promote integration would be timely

- finding a way of recognising the importance of strategic commissioning and planning, not just clinical involvement in commissioning at local level; there has been little research into the effectiveness of commissioning of different types of services and at different scales of population; some that looks at the ability of PCTs to bring about their planned service changes is nearing publication, but more research is needed to inform the development of commissioning including clinical senates which are intended to augment the range of clinical advice available locally

- determining the relationship and balance between individual patient choice as a driver of efficiency/quality (competition in the market), and commissioners contracting for services by, for instance, tendering (competition for the market)

- developing services for people with complex chronic conditions that require co-ordination between providers in a system hitherto designed primarily to encourage supplier competition in a market for elective care

- developing ways of paying for outcomes and/or quality standards rather than purely for hospital activity (eg, paying for entire services through years of care that require inter-organisational collaboration, or altering the tariff to take account of quality measures)

- identifying the services and situations in which price competition could be positive for quality and efficiency, and those where this was not the case and prices should be fixed, as under PbR

- strengthening the system of quality regulation, and research into the effectiveness of regulation, so that decisions can be taken about whether there is a need for more inspections and greater voice for patients and relatives to express concerns, or whether reliance on triggers from routine performance indicators is sufficient

- identifying situations and services where market competition is clearly positive for quality and efficiency, and where it is not and should be avoided to be replaced by alternatives such as benchmark competition.

Implementation

Although the coalition's policies are still very much in the design phase, it is important that policy-makers consider the issues of implementation at this stage. The key lessons from the review of implementation of the market reforms under New Labour suggest that the government should:

- pay attention to phasing and sequencing – consider which elements need to be in place first for the reforms to succeed

- commission appropriate research to assess the impacts of the main policy changes

- be open to adaptation and refinement of policies in response to the changing context, feedback from implementers and findings of evaluation studies

- have a clear narrative about the reforms and make sure their purpose is clear not only to civil servants but to those responsible for implementing them

- expect the reforms to be diluted during implementation and therefore give them a decent chance to work

- expect there to be unintended consequences and a need to amplify the positive and mitigate the negative

- recognise where the inherent tensions and points of conflict are between objectives and policy instruments, and try to resolve them at least in the minds of those responsible for local implementation

- recognise that 'context matters' – while geography might not be such a problem, current market structures will have an impact, as will cultures and institutions – so allow scope for the reforms to look different in different settings

- recognise that choice and competition may have limited application beyond elective care – different approaches and new currencies may be needed to promote better care for people with long-term conditions, complex needs and mental health problems

- not assume that passing new legislation will change the behaviour of those within the system, or not immediately, and not necessarily in the ways predicted

- recognise that new policies are usually layered upon existing policies, thus limiting their effects: the stripping away of performance management under the proposed reforms may mean providers 'look out rather than up', as they did during this period of reform under New Labour; active steps will be needed to change managerial cultures and relationships if this is to alter.

Conclusion

Overall, those who were responsible for designing and implementing the market reforms between 2002 and 2010 can take some consolation from the findings presented in this book. The market appears not to have had the most obvious negative effects predicted by many of the critics. Where there has been an effect, it has largely been in line with the expectations of proponents. The problem, if it *is* a problem, is that these reforms had only a small, sometimes imperceptible, impact in the desired directions. Their scope has also largely been limited to elective services, and their reach has varied geographically: those at local level have not always understood what was intended, or have not responded to the incentives – in some cases actively resisting them.

This lack of a major observed effect may be partly due to the time lag between the reforms being conceived and enacted, their implementation, and the visibility of the impact. The market was only partially functioning for much of this period, and some of the effects that were observed – such as those reported by Gaynor *et al* (2011) – appeared only towards the end of the period.

Although the effects of the Labour government's market reforms (2002–10) set out in this book were not dramatic, there is evidence to suggest that they were beginning to have some positive impact. However, almost nothing is known about the costs of competition or its relative effect compared to other approaches such as targets and performance management. The issue, then, for policy-makers is whether the costs, both financial and political, are worth the effort, if these reforms achieve limited change.

As we have shown, some parts of the reforms are more strongly based on what we have learned than others, and there are important judgements to be made about the extent and pace of any further shift towards a more market-led system.

First, policy-makers need to decide whether the extension and development of the market is suited to a period of consolidation and dramatic financial tightening. The context in which the Labour government's market reforms were implemented was one of growth, in which the main public concern and challenge at the start of the period was timely access to care and, later on in the process, to ensure that new capacity was well used.

Second, policy-makers have to judge whether these reforms help the NHS better meet the needs of an ageing population, many of whom have multiple chronic diseases, some of whom have complex health and social care needs, and an increasing proportion have dementia. Labour's market reforms were largely applied to, and had most effect in, the area of elective surgery. If the priority now is to make the health system responsive to the needs of those with ongoing physical and mental health needs, then competition may need to be complemented by other approaches (eg, various forms of so-called integrated care).

Policy sometimes struggles to adapt to a changing context, while the politicians who conceive of and enact reforms have often already moved on by the time the consequences of their actions become visible. However, over the next decade, the impact of the financial situation the NHS finds itself in is likely to overshadow any consequences of further market reforms.

References

Aakvik A, Kjerstad E (2005). 'The Effect of Reimbursement Incentives on DRG Creep in Norwegian Hospitals'. Poster presented at the International Health Economics Association's Fifth World Congress, 10–13 July. MO-0800-1700-Atrium: Poster-1. Available at: www.healtheconomics.org/barcelona/abstractbook2005.pdf (accessed on 10 May 2011).

Abbasi K (1998). 'Butchers and gropers'. *British Medical Journal*, vol 317, no 7172, p 1599. Available at: www.bmj.com/content/317/7172/1599.3.full (accessed on 10 May 2011).

Abraham JM, Gaynor M, Vogt WB (2007). 'Entry and competition in local hospital markets'. *Journal of Industrial Economics*, vol 55, no 2, pp 265–88. Available at: http://onlinelibrary.wiley.com/doi/10.1111/j.1467-6451.2007.00311.x/full (accessed on 10 May 2011).

Addicott R (2011). *Social Enterprise in Health Care: Promoting organisational autonomy and staff engagement*. London: The King's Fund.

Alberti G (2009). *Mid Staffordshire NHS Foundation Trust: A review of the procedures for emergency admissions and treatment, and progress against the recommendation of the March Healthcare Commission report*. London: Department of Health. Available at: www.monitor-nhsft.gov.uk/kt/ktwebservice/download.php?code=f87ee513717e01c5368b784160f2895651acaeff&d=1956&u= (accessed on 10 May 2011).

Allen P (2009). 'Restructuring the NHS again: supply side reform in recent English health care policy'. *Financial Accountability & Management*, vol 25, no 4, pp 373–89. Available at: http://onlinelibrary.wiley.com/doi/10.1111/j.1468-0408.2009.00483.x/full (accessed on 10 May 2011).

Allen P (2006). 'New localism in the English National Health Service: what is it for?'. *Health Policy*, vol 79, no 2, pp 244–52. Available at: www.healthpolicyjrnl.com/article/S0168-8510%2806%2900009-1/abstract (accessed on 10 May 2011).

Allen P (2002). 'A socio-legal and economic analysis of contracting in the NHS internal market using a case study of contracting for district nursing'. *Social Science & Medicine*, vol 54, no 2, pp 255–66. Available at: www.sciencedirect.com/science?_ob=ArticleURL&_udi=B6VBF-44HTGB4-8&_user=10&_coverDate=01%2F31%2F2002&_rdoc=1&_fmt=high&_orig=gateway&_

origin=gateway&_sort=d&_docanchor=&view=c&_searchStrId=1745669682&_
rerunOrigin=google&_acct=C000050221&_version=1&_urlVersion=0&_userid=
10&md5=7d4f6e29970a0fe237a5300412a7cf5b&searchtype=a (accessed on
10 May 2011).

Allen P, Bartlett W, Pérotin V, Zamora B, Turner S (2011a). 'New forms of
provider in the English National Health Service'. *Annals of Public and Cooperative
Economics*, vol 82, no 1, pp 77–95. Available at: http://onlinelibrary.wiley.com/
doi/10.1111/j.1467-8292.2010.00431.x/abstract (accessed on 10 May 2011).

Allen P, Wright J, Keen J, Dempster PG, Hutchings A, Townsend J, Street A,
Verzulli R (2011b). *Investigating the Governance of NHS Foundation Trusts.* Final
report. National Institute for Health Research Service Delivery and Organisation
programme. London: HMSO. Available at: www.sdo.nihr.ac.uk/files/project/SDO_
ES_08-1618-157_V01.pdf (accessed on 10 May 2011).

Alvarez-Rosete A, Bevan G, Mays N, Dixon J (2005). 'Effect of diverging policy
across the NHS'. *British Medical Journal*, vol 331, no 7522, pp 946–50.

Anderson K (2006). *Independent Sector Treatment Centres. A report from
Ken Anderson, Commercial Director, Department of Health, to the Secretary of
State for Health.* London: Department of Health. Available at: www.dh.gov.uk/
prod_consum_dh/groups/dh_digitalassets/@dh/@en/documents/digitalasset/
dh_4129108.pdf (accessed on 10 May 2011).

Appleby J, Ham C, Imison C, Jennings M (2010). *Improving NHS Productivity:
More with the same not more of the same.* London: The King's Fund.

Appleby J, Renu J (2004). 'Payment by Results: the NHS financial revolution'. *New
Economy*, vol 11, pp 195–200.

Appleby J, Robertson R (2010). 'A healthy improvement? Satisfaction with the
NHS under Labour', in Park A, Phillips M, Clery E, Curtice J (eds), *British Social
Attitudes Survey 2010–2011: Exploring Labour's legacy – the 27th report.* London:
Sage. Available at: www.download-it.org/learning-resources.php?promoCode=
&partnerID=&content=story&fixedmetadataID=&storyID=26048 (accessed on
10 May 2011).

Appleby J, Crawford R, Emmerson C (2009). *How Cold Will it be? Prospects for
NHS funding: 2011–2017.* London: The King's Fund.

Appleby J, Smith A, Devlin N, Parkin P (2005). 'Effects on activity and waiting
times of a new fixed price activity-based reimbursement system for English NHS
hospitals'. Poster presented at 5th World Congress of the International Health
Economics Association, Barcelona, July.

Appleby J, Harrison A, Devlin N (2003). *What is the Real Cost of More Patient
Choice?* London: The King's Fund. Available at: www.kingsfund.org.uk/document.
rm?id=84 (accessed on 10 May 2011).

Ashton T (1998). 'Contracting for health services in New Zealand: a transaction cost analysis'. *Social Science & Medicine*, vol 46, no 3, pp 357–67.

Audit Commission (2009). *More for Less? Are productivity and efficiency improving in the NHS?* London: Audit Commission. Available at: www.audit-commission. gov.uk/SiteCollectionDocuments/AuditCommissionReports/NationalStudies/200 91111moreforless.pdf (accessed on 10 May 2011).

Audit Commission (2008a). *Auditors' Local Evaluation 2007/08: Summary results for NHS trusts and primary care trusts.* London: Audit Commission. Available at: www.audit-commission.gov.uk/SiteCollectionDocuments/ AuditCommissionReports/NationalStudies/ALEBriefing2October2008.pdf (accessed on 14 May 2011).

Audit Commission (2008b). *The Right Result? Payment by Results 2003–07.* London: Audit Commission. Available at: www.audit-commission.gov.uk/ SiteCollectionDocuments/AuditCommissionReports/NationalStudies/The_right_ result_PbR_2008.pdf (accessed on 10 May 2011).

Audit Commission (2007). *Putting Commissioning into Practice: Implementing practice based commissioning through good financial management.* London: Audit Commission. Available at: www.audit-commission.gov.uk/ SiteCollectionDocuments/AuditCommissionReports/NationalStudies/Puttingcom missioningintopractice_22Nov2007REPORT.pdf (accessed on 10 May 2011).

Audit Commission (2006). *Early Lessons In Implementing Practice Based Commissioning: Key areas to focus on for success and key questions for primary care trusts' boards to consider.* London: Audit Commission. Available at: www. audit-commission.gov.uk/SiteCollectionDocuments/AuditCommissionReports/ NationalStudies/PBC_earlylessons.pdf (accessed on 10 May 2011).

Audit Commission (2005). *Early Lessons From Payment By Results.* London: Audit Commission. Available at: www.audit-commission.gov.uk/ SiteCollectionDocuments/AuditCommissionReports/NationalStudies/ EarlyLessonsFromPaymentByResults11OCT05REP.pdf (accessed on 28 May 2011).

Audit Commission and Healthcare Commission (2008). *Is the Treatment Working? Progress with the NHS system reform programme.* London: Audit Commission. Available at: www.audit-commission.gov.uk/SiteCollectionDocuments/ AuditCommissionReports/NationalStudies/IstheTreatmentWorking.pdf (accessed on 10 May 2011).

Auditor General for Wales (2006). *Ambulance Services in Wales.* Cardiff: National Audit Office Wales. Available at: www.wao.gov.uk/assets/englishdocuments/ Ambulance_Inquiry.pdf (accessed on 10 May 2011).

Auditor General for Wales (2005). *NHS Waiting Times in Wales. Volume 1 – The scale of the problem.* Cardiff: National Audit Office Wales. Available at: www.wao. gov.uk/assets/englishdocuments/NHS_Waiting_Times_Vol_1_agw_2005.pdf (accessed on 10 May 2011).

Ayres I, Braithwaite J (1992). *Responsive Regulation: Transcending the deregulation debate.* Oxford: Oxford University Press.

Baggott R (1997). 'Evaluating health care reform: the case of the NHS internal market'. *Public Administration*, vol 75, no 2, pp 283–306.

Baldrige (2011). 'Baldrige Performance Excellence Program'. Baldrige website. Available at: www.nist.gov/baldrige/ (accessed on 10 June 2011).

Bardsley M, Spiegelhalter DJ, Blunt I, Chitnis X, Roberts A, Bharania S (2009). 'Using routine intelligence to target inspection of healthcare providers in England'. *Quality and Safety in Health Care*, vol 18, no 3, pp 189–94.

Barnett J, Ogden J, Daniells E (2008). 'The value of choice: a qualitative study'. *British Journal of General Practice*, vol 58, no 554, pp 609–13. Available at: www. ncbi.nlm.nih.gov/pmc/articles/PMC2529197/ (accessed on 10 May 2011).

Barr DA, Fenton L, Blane D (2008).'The claim for patient choice and equity'. *Journal of Medical Ethics*, vol 34, no 4, pp 271–4.

Bartlett W, Allen P, Pérotin V, Turner S, Zamora B, Matchaya G, Roberts J (2011). *Provider Diversity in the NHS: Impact on quality and innovation.* Report for the Department of Health Policy Research Programme.

Benson L, Boyd A, Walshe K (2004). *Learning from CHI: The impact of healthcare regulation.* Manchester: Manchester Centre for Healthcare Management, University of Manchester. Available at: www.escholar.manchester.ac.uk/api/ datastream?publicationPid=uk-ac-man-scw:118432&datastreamId=FULL-TEXT. PDF (accessed on 10 May 2011).

Besley T, Ghatak M (2003). *Incentives, Choice and Accountability in the Provision of Public Services.* London: Institute for Fiscal Studies. Available at: www.ifs.org. uk/wps/wp0308.pdf (accessed on 10 May 2011).

Besley TJ, Bevan G, Burchardi K (2009). *Naming and Shaming: The impacts of different regimes on hospital waiting times in England and Wales.* Centre for Economic Policy Research Discussion Paper No DP7306. London: Centre for Economic Policy Research. Available at: http://ssrn.com/abstract=1433902 (accessed on 10 May 2011).

Bevan G (2010). 'Approaches and impacts of different systems of assessing hospital performance'. *Journal of Comparative Policy Analysis*, vol 12, no 1–2, pp 33–56.

Bevan G (2009). 'Have targets done more harm than good in the English NHS? No'. *British Medical Journal*, vol 338, p a3129. Available at: www.bmj.com/cgi/ content/full/338/jan16_2/a3129?maxtoshow=andHITS=10andhits=10andRESUL

TFORMAT=1andauthor1=Bevanandandorexacttitle=andandandorexacttitleabs=a ndandandorexactfulltext=andandsearchid=1andFIRSTINDEX=0andsortspec=rele vanceandfdate=1/1/2009andresourcetype=HWCIT (accessed on 10 May 2011).

Bevan G (2008). 'Changing paradigms of governance and regulation of quality of healthcare in England'. *Health Risk & Society*, vol 10, no 1, pp 85–101.

Bevan G (2006). 'Setting targets for health care performance: lessons from a case study of the English NHS'. *National Institute Economic Review*, vol 197, no 1, pp 67–79. Available at: http://ner.sagepub.com/content/197/1/67.2.abstract (accessed on 10 May 2011).

Bevan G, Cornwell J (2006). 'Structure and logic of regulation and governance of quality of health care: was OFSTED a model for the Commission for Health Improvement?' *Health Economics, Policy and Law*, vol 1, no 4, pp 343–70.

Bevan G, Hamblin R (2009). 'Hitting and missing targets by ambulance services for emergency calls: effects of different systems of performance measurement within the UK'. *Journal of the Royal Statistical Society, Series A (Statistics in Society)*, vol 172, no 1, pp 161–90.

Bevan G, Hood C (2006a). 'Have targets improved performance in the English NHS?'. *British Medical Journal*, vol 332, no 7538, pp 419–22.

Bevan G, Hood C (2006b). 'What's measured is what matters: targets and gaming in the English public health care system'. *Public Administration*, vol 84, no 3, pp 517–38.

Bird SM (2009). 'Buried data and the UK Healthcare Commission's legacy'. *Lancet*, vol 373: pp1604–5.

Birk HO, Onsberg Henriksen L (2006). 'Why do not all hip- and knee patients facing long waiting times accept re-referral to hospitals with short waiting time? Questionnaire study'. *Health Policy*, vol 77, no 3, pp 318–25.

Bloom N, Propper C, Seiler S, Van Reenen J (2010). *The Impact of Competition on Management Quality: Evidence from Public Hospitals*, NBER Working Paper no 16032. Cambridge, MA: National Bureau of Economic Research.

Blunt I, Bardsley M, Dixon J (2010). *Trends in Emergency Admissions in England 2004–2009: Is greater efficiency breeding inefficiency?* London: The Nuffield Trust. Available at: www.nuffieldtrust.org.uk/publications/detail.aspx?id=145&PRid=714 (accessed on 10 May 2011).

Boyce T, Dixon A, Fasolo B, Reutskaja E (2010). *Choosing a High-quality Hospital: The role of nudges, scorecard design and information*. London: The King's Fund.

Boyle S (2011). 'United Kingdom (England) health system review'. *Health Systems in Transition*, vol 13, no 1, pp 1–483. Available at: http://maciej.bioinfo.pl/ pmid:21454148 (accessed on 14 May 2011).

Boyle S (2007). 'Payment by results in England'. *Eurohealth*, vol 13, no 1, pp 12–16.

Brereton L, Gubb J (2010). *Refusing Treatment: The NHS and market-based reforms*. London: Civitas. Available at: www.civitas.org.uk/pdf/RefusingTreatment. pdf (accessed on 10 May 2011).

British Medical Association (2009). *Choose and Book – Learning lessons from local experience*. London: British Medical Association. Available at: www.bma.org.uk/ images/chooseandbook_tcm41-181729.pdf (accessed on 10 May 2011).

Browne J, Jamieson L, Lewsey J, Van der Meulen J, Copley L, Black N (2008). 'Case-mix and patients' reports of outcome in independent sector treatment centres: comparison with NHS providers'. *BMC Health Services Research*, vol 8, no 78. Available at: www.biomedcentral.com/content/pdf/1472-6963-8-78.pdf (accessed on 10 May 2011).

Burge P, Devlin N, Appleby J, Gallo F, Nason E, Ling T (2006). *Understanding Patients' Choices at the Point of Referral*. Cambridge: RAND Europe. Available at: www.rand.org/content/dam/rand/pubs/technical_reports/2006/RAND_TR359. pdf (accessed on 10 May 2011).

Butler J (1992). *Patients, Policies and Politics: Before and after Working for Patients*. Buckingham: Open University Press.

Cabinet Office/Department of Health (2003). *'Making a Difference': Reducing burdens in healthcare inspection and monitoring*. London: The Cabinet Office. Available at: www.dh.gov.uk/prod_consum_dh/groups/dh_digitalassets/ documents/digitalasset/dh_078473.pdf (accessed on 10 May 2011).

Campbell-Smith D (2008). *Follow the Money: The Audit Commission, public money and the management of public services, 1983–2008*. London: Penguin Allen Lane.

Care Quality Commission (2011). 'What We Do'. Care Quality Commission website. Available at: www.cqc.org.uk/aboutcqc/whatwedo.cfm (accessed on 8 June 2011).

Care Quality Commission (2009). *NHS Performance Ratings 2008/09. An overview of the performance of NHS trusts in England*. London: Care Quality Commission. Available at: www.cqc.org.uk/_db/_documents/0809_NHS_ratings_overview_ document_161009_200910164847.pdf (accessed on 10 May 2011).

Carey K (2000). 'Hospital cost containment and length of stay: an econometric analysis'. *Southern Economic Journal*, vol 67, no 2, pp 363–80. Available at: www. jstor.org/pss/1061475 (accessed on 10 May 2011).

Carter GM, Newhouse JP, Relles DA (1990). 'How much change in the Case Mix Index is DRG creep?'. *Journal of Health Economics*, vol 9, no 4, pp 411–28.

Chalkley M, Malcomson JM (2000). 'Government purchasing of health services', in Culyer AJ, Newhouse JP (eds), *Handbook of Health Economics*, vol 1A, part 1, chapter 15, pp 847–90. Amsterdam: Elsevier.

Charpentier C, Samuelson L (1996). 'Effects of new control systems in Swedish health care organizations'. *Financial Accountability & Management*, vol 12, no 2, pp 157–71.

Chernew M, Scanlon D, Hayward R (1998). 'Insurance type and choice of hospital for coronary artery bypass graft surgery'. *Health Services Research*, vol 33, no 3 (part 1), pp 447–66.

Chisholm A, Redding D, Cross P, Coulter A (2007). *Patient and Public Involvement in PCT Commissioning: A survey of primary care trusts*. Oxford: Picker Institute Europe.

Clarke J, Newman J, Westmorland L (2008). 'The antagonisms of choice: new Labour and the reform of public services'. *Social Policy and Society*, vol 7, no 2, pp 245–53.

Clarke J, Smith N, Vidler E (2006). 'The indeterminacy of choice: political, policy and organisational implications'. *Social Policy and Society*, vol 5, pp 327–36.

Coleman A, Checkland K, Harrison S, Dowswell G (2009). *Practice-Based Commissioning – Theory, implementation and outcome*. Final report. University of Manchester: National Primary Care Research and Development Centre.

Coleman A, Harrison S, Checkland K, Hiroeh U (2007). *Practice Based Commissioning: Report of a survey of primary care trusts*. Manchester: National Primary Care Research and Development Centre. Available at: www.medicine. manchester.ac.uk/primarycare/npcrdc-archive/Publications/PBC_report_Dec07. pdf (accessed on 20 June 2001).

Colin Thomé D (2009). *Mid Staffordshire NHS Foundation Trust: A review of lessons learnt for commissioners and performance managers following the Healthcare Commission investigation* [online]. Department of Health website. Available at: www.dh.gov.uk/prod_consum_dh/groups/dh_digitalassets/documents/ digitalasset/dh_098661.pdf (accessed on 10 May 2011).

Commission for Health Improvement (2011). 'Acute Trust Overview'. Commission for Health Improvement website. Available at: www.chi.nhs.uk/Ratings/Trust/ Overview/acute_overview.asp (accessed on 8 June 2011).

Commission for Health Improvement (2004a). *A Commentary on Star Ratings 2002/2003*. London: Commission for Health Improvement. Available at: www.chi. nhs.uk/Ratings/Downloads/ratings_commentary.pdf (accessed on 10 May 2011).

Commission for Health Improvement (2004b). *What CHI Has Found In: Acute services*. Sector report. London: Commission for Health Improvement. Available at: www.chai.org.uk/_db/_documents/04001542.pdf (accessed on 10 May 2011).

Commission for Health Improvement (2004c). *What CHI Has Found In: Primary care trusts*. Sector report. London: Commission for Health Improvement. Available at: www.chai.org.uk/_db/_documents/04001441.pdf (accessed on 10 May 2011).

Commission for Health Improvement (2003). 'Performance indicators and ratings for 2002/2003'. Commission for Health Improvement/Healthcare Commission website. Available at: http://ratings2003.healthcarecommission.org.uk/ratings/ (accessed on 10 May 2011).

Commission for Health Improvement (2002a). *Report of A Clinical Governance Review at Maidstone and Tunbridge Wells NHS Trust*. London: The Stationery Office.

Commission for Health Improvement (2002b). *Report of a Clinical Governance Review at Mid Staffordshire General NHS Trust*. London: The Stationery Office.

Commission for Health Improvement (2002c). *Report of a Clinical Governance Review at Stoke Mandeville Hospital NHS Trust*. London: The Stationery Office. Available at: www.chai.org.uk/_db/_documents/04005978.pdf (accessed on 10 May 2011).

Commission for Health Improvement (2000). *A Guide to Clinical Governance Reviews*. London: Commission for Health Improvement.

Commonwealth Fund Commission on a High Performance Health System (2006). *Framework For a High Performance Health System for the United States*. New York: The Commonwealth Fund. Available at: www.commonwealthfund.org/~/media/Files/Publications/Fund%20Report/2006/Aug/Framework%20for%20a%20High%20Performance%20Health%20System%20for%20the%20United%20States/Commission_framework_high_performance_943%20pdf.pdf (accessed on 10 May 2011).

Conner-Spady B, Sanmartin C, Johnston G, McGurran J, Kehler M, Noseworthy T (2008). 'Willingness of patients to change surgeons for a shorter waiting time for joint arthroplasty'. *Canadian Medical Association Journal*, vol 179, no 4, pp 327–32.

Connolly S, Bevan G, Mays N (2010). *Funding and Performance of Healthcare Systems in the Four Countries of the UK Before and After Devolution*. London: The Nuffield Trust. Available at: www.nuffieldtrust.org.uk/publications/detail.aspx?id=0&PRid=675 (accessed on 11 May 2011).

Connor RA, Feldman RD, Dowd BE (1998). 'The effects of market concentration and horizontal mergers on hospital costs and prices'. *International Journal of the Economics of Business*, vol 5, no 2, pp 159–80.

Cookson R, Laudicella M (2011). 'Do the poor cost much more? The relationship between small area income deprivation and length of stay for elective hip replacement in the English NHS from 2001/2 to 2007/8'. *Social Science and Medicine*, vol 72, no 2, pp 173–84.

Cookson R, Dusheiko M, Hardman G, Martin S (2010a). 'Competition and inequality: evidence from the English National Health Service 1991–2001'. *Journal of Public Administration, Research and Theory*, vol 20, suppl 2, pp 181–205.

Cookson R, Laudicella M, Li Donni P (2010b). 'Did increased competition undermine socio-economic equity in hospital care in the English National Health Service from 2003 to 2008? Panel analysis of small area administrative data'. Paper presented to the Health Economists Study Group Meeting, York, January 2011.

Cooper ZN, Gibbons S, Jones S, McGuire A (2011). 'Does hospital competition save lives? Evidence from the English NHS patient choice reforms'. *The Economic Journal*, vol 121, pp F228-60.

Cooper ZN, Gibbons S, Jones S, McGuire A (2010). *Does Hospital Competition Improve Efficiency? An analysis of the recent market-based reforms to the English NHS*. CEP discussion paper 988. London: Centre for Economic Performance, London School of Economics and Political Science, London, UK. Available at: http://eprints.lse.ac.uk/28578/1/dp0988.pdf (accessed on 10 May 2011).

Cooper ZN, McGuire A, Jones S, Le Grand J (2009). 'Equity, waiting times, and NHS reforms: retrospective study'. *British Medical Journal*, vol 339, p b3264. Available at: www.bmj.com/content/339/bmj.b3264.full.pdf?sid=65acc8fc-c138-4fbd-9596-ac3dfd12e6d0 (accessed on 10 May 2011).

Co-operation and Competition Panel (2011). *Review of the Operation of 'Any Willing Provider' for the Provision of Routine Elective Care: Interim assessment*. Available at: www.ccpanel.org.uk/content/cases/Operation_of_any_willing_provider_for_the_provision_of_routine_elective_care_under_free_choice/110224_AWP_Interim_Assessment_Final.pdf (accessed on 1 July 2011).

Coulter A, Bradlow J (1993). 'Effect of NHS reforms on general practitioners' referral patterns'. *British Medical Journal*, vol 306, pp 433–6. Available at: www.bmj.com/content/306/6875/433.full.pdf?sid=bd1a9b4c-2470-4fc0-afa3-28a6c3b3481f (accessed on 10 May 2011).

Coulter A, Collins A (2011). *Making Shared Decision-making a Reality: No decision about me without me*. London: The King's Fund.

Coulter A, Le Maistre N, Henderson L (2005). *Patients' Experience of Choosing Where to Undergo Surgical Treatment: Evaluation of London Patient Choice Scheme*. Oxford: Picker Institute Europe.

Crisp N (2005). *Commissioning A Patient-Led NHS. Letter to chief executives of NHS organisations, chief executives of local authorities, directors of social services and primary care trust, PEC chairs*. London: Department of Health. Available at: www.dh.gov.uk/prod_consum_dh/groups/dh_digitalassets/@dh/@en/documents/digitalasset/dh_4116717.pdf (accessed on 10 May 2011).

Croxson B (1999). *Organisational Costs in the New NHS: An introduction to the transaction costs and internal costs of delivering health care*. London: Office of Health Economics.

Croxson B, Propper C, Perkins A (2001). 'Do doctors respond to financial incentives? UK family doctors and the GP fundholder scheme'. *Journal of Public Economics*, vol 79, pp 375–98.

Crump H (2008). 'PCTs failing to decommission services'. *Health Service Journal*, 9 October. Available at: www.hsj.co.uk/news/pcts-failing-to-decommission-services/1890661.article (accessed on 10 May 2011).

Curry N, Ham C (2010). *Clinical and Service Integration: The route to improved outcomes*. London: The King's Fund. Available at: www.kingsfund.org.uk/publications/clinical_and_service.html (accessed on 11 July 2011).

Curry N, Goodwin N, Naylor C, Robertson R (2008). *Practice-Based Commissioning: Reinvigorate, replace or abandon?* London: The King's Fund. Available at: www.kingsfund.org.uk/document.rm?id=8129 (accessed on 10 May 2011).

Dafny LS (2005). 'How do hospitals respond to price changes?'. *The American Economic Review*, vol 95, no 5, pp 1525–47. Available at: www.aeaweb.org/articles.php?doi=10.1257/000282805775014236 (accessed on 10 May 2011).

Darzi A (2007). *Healthcare for London: A framework for action*. London: NHS London. Available at: http://healthcareforlondon.steel-ltd.com/assets/Publications/A-Framework-for-Action/aFrameworkForAction.pdf (accessed on 11 May 2011).

Davidson S, Evans P (2010). *NHS Unlimited? Who runs our GP services. A study of GP services put out to tender by the NHS*. Brighton: NHS Support Federation. Available at: www.nhscampaign.org/uploads/documents/NHS%20Unlimited.pdf (accessed on 10 May 2011).

Davies HT (2002). 'Understanding organizational culture in reforming the National Health Service'. *Journal of the Royal Society of Medicine*, vol 95, no 3, pp 140–2.

Dawson D, Jacobs R, Martin S, Smith P (2004). *Evaluation of the London Patient Choice Project: System wide impacts*. Final report. York: University of York.

Day P, Klein R (2005). *Governance of Foundation Trusts: Dilemmas of diversity*. London: The Nuffield Trust. Available at: www.nuffieldtrust.org.uk/publications/detail.aspx?id=0&PRid=156 (accessed on 10 May 2011).

Day P, Klein R (2004). *The NHS Improvers: A study of the Commission for Health Improvement*. London: The King's Fund. Available at: www.kingsfund.org.uk/document.rm?id=120 (accessed on 10 May 2011).

Day P, Klein R (2001). *Auditing the Auditors: Audit in the National Health Service*. London: The Nuffield Trust. Available at: www.nuffieldtrust.org.uk/publications/detail.aspx?id=0&PRid=58 (accessed on 10 May 2011).

Department of Health (2011a). *Government Response to the NHS Future Forum Report*. Cm 8113. London: The Stationery Office. Available at: www.dh.gov.uk/prod_consum_dh/groups/dh_digitalassets/documents/digitalasset/dh_127719.pdf (accessed on 1 July 2011).

Department of Health (2011b). *Government Response to the NHS Future Forum report: Briefing notes on amendments to the Health and Social Care Bill* [online].

Department of Health website. Available at www.dh.gov.uk/prod_consum_dh/groups/dh_digitalassets/documents/digitalasset/dh_127880.pdf (accessed on 1 July 2011).

Department of Health (2011c). *Making Quality Your Business: A guide to the right to provide* [online]. Available at: www.dh.gov.uk/prod_consum_dh/groups/dh_digitalassets/documents/digitalasset/dh_125638.pdf (accessed on 1 July 2011).

Department of Health (2010a). *Equity and Excellence: Liberating the NHS.* Cm 7881. London: The Stationery Office. Available at: www.dh.gov.uk/prod_consum_dh/groups/dh_digitalassets/@dh/@en/@ps/documents/digitalasset/dh_117794.pdf (accessed on 16 May 2011).

Department of Health (2010b). *Liberating the NHS: An information revolution: a consultation on proposals.* London: Department of Health. Available at: www.dh.gov.uk/prod_consum_dh/groups/dh_digitalassets/@dh/@en/documents/digitalasset/dh_120598.pdf (accessed on 10 May 2011).

Department of Health (2010c). *Liberating the NHS: Commissioning for patients: a consultation on proposals.* London: Department of Health. Available at: www.dh.gov.uk/en/Consultations/Closedconsultations/DH_117587 (accessed on 8 July 2011).

Department of Health (2010d). *Liberating the NHS: Greater choice and control: a consultation on proposals.* London: Department of Health. Available at: www.dh.gov.uk/en/Consultations/Liveconsultations/DH_119651 (accessed on 13 May 2011).

Department of Health (2010e). *Liberating the NHS: Report of the arm's-length bodies review.* London: Department of Health. Available at: www.dh.gov.uk/prod_consum_dh/groups/dh_digitalassets/@dh/@en/@ps/documents/digitalasset/dh_118053.pdf (accessed on 12 May 2011).

Department of Health (2010f). *Payment by Results Guidance for 2010–11.* London: Department of Health. Available at: www.parliament.uk/deposits/depositedpapers/2010/DEP2010-1594.pdf (accessed on 10 May 2011).

Department of Health (2010g). 'Practice-based commissioning group and independent leads survey: Wave 3'. Department of Health website. Available at: www.dh.gov.uk/en/Publicationsandstatistics/Publications/PublicationsStatistics/DH_117071 (accessed on 19 August 2011).

Department of Health (2010h). *Report on the National Patient Choice Survey – February 2010 England* [online]. Department of Health website. Available at: www.dh.gov.uk/prod_consum_dh/groups/dh_digitalassets/documents/digitalasset/dh_117096.pdf (accessed on 10 May 2011).

Department of Health (2009a). *NHS 2010–2015: From good to great. Preventative, people-centred, productive.* Cm 7775. London: The Stationery Office. Available at: www.dh.gov.uk/prod_consum_dh/groups/dh_digitalassets/@dh/@en/@ps/@sta/@perf/documents/digitalasset/dh_109887.pdf (accessed on 10 May 2011).

Department of Health (2009b). *Report on the National Patient Choice Survey – March 2009 England* [online]. Department of Health website. Available at: www.dh.gov.uk/prod_consum_dh/groups/dh_digitalassets/documents/digitalasset/dh_103681.pdf (accessed on 10 May 2011).

Department of Health (2009c). *Tackling Health Inequalities: 10 years on – a review of developments in tackling health inequalities in England over the last 10 years.* London: Central Office of Information. Available at: www.dh.gov.uk/prod_consum_dh/groups/dh_digitalassets/documents/digitalasset/dh_098934.pdf (accessed on 10 May 2011).

Department of Health (2008a). *Health Inequalities: Progress and next steps.* London: Central Office of Information. Available at: www.dh.gov.uk/prod_consum_dh/groups/dh_digitalassets/@dh/@en/documents/digitalasset/dh_085312.pdf (accessed on 10 May 2011).

Department of Health (2008b). *ISTC Phase 1 Contractual Information (as at end of September 2007/08)* [online]. Department of Health website. Available at: www.dh.gov.uk/prod_consum_dh/idcplg%3FIdcService=GET_FILE&dID=154015&Rendition=Web (accessed on 10 May 2011).

Department of Health (2008c). *ISTC Phase 2 Contractual Information (as at September 2008)* [online]. Department of Health website. Available at: www.dh.gov.uk/en/Healthcare/Primarycare/Treatmentcentres/index.htm?IdcService=GET_FILE&dID=178488&Rendition=Web (accessed on 10 May 2011).

Department of Health (2007a). *Johnson Outlines New Measures to Deliver More Choice and Faster Treatment to Patients.* Press release, 15 November. London: Department of Health.

Department of Health (2007b). *Report on the National Patient Choice Survey – March 2007 England* [online]. Department of Health website. Available at: www.dh.gov.uk/prod_consum_dh/groups/dh_digitalassets/documents/digitalasset/dh_077467.pdf (accessed on 10 May 2011).

Department of Health (2007b). *The NHS in England: The Operating Framework for 2008/09.* London: Department of Health. Available at: www.dh.gov.uk/prod_consum_dh/groups/dh_digitalassets/@dh/@en/documents/digitalasset/dh_081271.pdf (accessed on 21 May 2011).

Department of Health (2007c). *Welcoming Social Enterprise into Health and Social Care: A resource pack for social enterprise providers and commissioners.* London: Central Office of Information. Available at: www.dh.gov.uk/prod_consum_dh/groups/dh_digitalassets/@dh/@en/documents/digitalasset/dh_072927.pdf (accessed on 10 May 2011).

Department of Health (2007d). *World Class Commissioning: Competencies.* London: Department of Health. Available at: www.dh.gov.uk/prod_consum_dh/

groups/dh_digitalassets/documents/digitalasset/dh_080954.pdf (accessed on 10 May 2011).

Department of Health (2006a). *Our Health, Our Care, Our Say: A new direction for community services.* Cm 6737. White Paper. Norwich: The Stationery Office. Available at: http://webarchive.nationalarchives.gov.uk/+/www.dh.gov.uk/en/Publicationsandstatistics/Publications/PublicationsPolicyAndGuidance/DH_4127453 (accessed on 10 May 2011).

Department of Health (2006b). *Practice Based Commissioning: Practical implementation.* London: Department of Health. Available at: www.dh.gov.uk/prod_consum_dh/groups/dh_digitalassets/@dh/@en/@ps/@pub/@ppg/documents/digitalasset/dh_062706.pdf (accessed on 10 May 2011).

Department of Health (2006c). *The NHS in England: The operating framework for 2006/7.* London: Department of Health. Available at: www.dh.gov.uk/prod_consum_dh/groups/dh_digitalassets/@dh/@en/documents/digitalasset/dh_4127315.pdf (accessed on 10 May 2011).

Department of Health (2005a). *Health Reform in England: Update and next steps.* London: Central Office of Information. Available at: www.dh.gov.uk/prod_consum_dh/groups/dh_digitalassets/@dh/@en/documents/digitalasset/dh_4124727.pdf (accessed on 10 May 2011).

Department of Health (2005b). *Treatment Centres: Delivering faster, quality care and choice for NHS patients.* London: Department of Health. Available at: www.dh.gov.uk/prod_consum_dh/groups/dh_digitalassets/@dh/@en/documents/digitalasset/dh_4100524.pdf (accessed on 10 May 2011).

Department of Health (2004a). *'Choose & Book' – Patient's choice of hospital and booked appointment: policy framework for choice and booking at point of referral.* London: Department of Health. Available at: www.dh.gov.uk/prod_consum_dh/groups/dh_digitalassets/@dh/@en/documents/digitalasset/dh_4088352.pdf (accessed on 10 May 2011).

Department of Health (2004b). *Practice Based Commissioning: Engaging practices in commissioning.* London: Department of Health. Available at: www.dh.gov.uk/prod_consum_dh/groups/dh_digitalassets/@dh/@en/documents/digitalasset/dh_4090359.pdf (accessed on 10 May 2011).

Department of Health (2004c). *Standards for Better Health.* London: Department of Health. Available at: www.dh.gov.uk/prod_consum_dh/groups/dh_digitalassets/@dh/@en/documents/digitalasset/dh_4132991.pdf (accessed on 10 June 2011).

Department of Health (2004d). *The NHS Improvement Plan: Putting people at the heart of public services.* Cm 6268. London: Department of Health. Available at: www.dh.gov.uk/prod_consum_dh/groups/dh_digitalassets/@dh/@en/@ps/documents/digitalasset/dh_118572.pdf (accessed on 10 May 2011).

Department of Health (2003a). *Building on the Best: Choice responsiveness and equity in the NHS*. Cm 6079. London: The Stationery Office. Available at: www.dh.gov.uk/prod_consum_dh/groups/dh_digitalassets/@dh/@en/documents/digitalasset/dh_4068400.pdf (accessed on 10 May 2011).

Department of Health (2003b). *Tackling Health Inequalities: A programme for action*. Cm 6374. London: Department of Health. Available at: www.dh.gov.uk/prod_consum_dh/groups/dh_digitalassets/@dh/@en/documents/digitalasset/dh_4019362.pdf (accessed on 10 May 2011).

Department of Health (2002a). *Delivering the NHS Plan: Next steps on investment, next steps on reform*. Cm 5503. London: Stationery Office. Available at: www.dh.gov.uk/prod_consum_dh/groups/dh_digitalassets/@dh/@en/@ps/documents/digitalasset/dh_118524.pdf (accessed on 16 May 2011).

Department of Health (2002b). *Growing Capacity: Independent sector diagnosis and treatment centres*. London: Department of Health. Available at: www.dh.gov.uk/prod_consum_dh/groups/dh_digitalassets/@dh/@en/documents/digitalasset/dh_4020527.pdf (accessed on 10 May 2011).

Department of Health (2002c). *Learning from Bristol: The Department of Health's Response to the Report of the Public Inquiry into children's heart surgery at the Bristol Royal Infirmary 1984–1995*. Cm 5363. London: The Stationery Office. Available at: www.dh.gov.uk/prod_consum_dh/groups/dh_digitalassets/@dh/@en/documents/digitalasset/dh_4059479.pdf (accessed on 16 May 2011).

Department of Health (2002d). *NHS Performance Ratings: Acute trusts, specialist trusts, ambulance trusts, mental health trusts 2001/02*. London: Department of Health. Available at: www.dh.gov.uk/prod_consum_dh/groups/dh_digitalassets/@dh/@en/documents/digitalasset/dh_4059773.pdf (accessed on 14 May 2011).

Department of Health (2002e). *Reforming NHS Financial Flows: Introducing payment by results*. London: Department of Health. Available at: www.dh.gov.uk/prod_consum_dh/groups/dh_digitalassets/@dh/@en/documents/digitalasset/dh_4018704.pdf (accessed on 10 May 2011).

Department of Health (2002f). *Securing Service Delivery: Commissioning freedoms of primary care trusts*. Health Service Circular 2002/007. London: Department of Health. Available at: www.dh.gov.uk/prod_consum_dh/groups/dh_digitalassets/@dh/@en/documents/digitalasset/dh_4012216.pdf (accessed on 10 May 2011).

Department of Health (2001a). *NHS Performance Ratings: Acute trusts 2000/01*. London: Department of Health. Available at: www.dh.gov.uk/prod_consum_dh/groups/dh_digitalassets/@dh/@en/documents/digitalasset/dh_4077600.pdf (accessed on 14 May 2011).

Department of Health (2001b). *Shifting the Balance of Power Within the NHS: Securing delivery*. London: Department of Health. Available at: www.dh.gov.uk/prod_consum_dh/groups/dh_digitalassets/@dh/@en/documents/digitalasset/dh_4076522.pdf (accessed on 10 May 2011).

Department of Health (2000a). *For the Benefit of Patients – A concordat with the private and voluntary health care provider sector*. London: Her Majesty's Stationery Office. Available at: www.dh.gov.uk/prod_consum_dh/groups/dh_digitalassets/@dh/@en/documents/digitalasset/dh_4076781.pdf (accessed on 10 May 2011).

Department of Health (2000b). *The NHS Plan: A plan for investment, a plan for reform*. Cm 4818-I. London: The Stationery Office. Available at: www.dh.gov.uk/prod_consum_dh/groups/dh_digitalassets/@dh/@en/@ps/documents/digitalasset/dh_118522.pdf (accessed on 10 May 2011).

Department of Health (1998). *A First Class Service: Quality in the new NHS*. London: Department of Health. Available at: www.dh.gov.uk/en/Publicationsandstatistics/Publications/PublicationsPolicyAndGuidance/DH_4006902 (accessed on 12 May 2011).

Department of Health (1997). *The New NHS: Modern, dependable*. Cm 3807. London: The Stationery Office. Available at: www.archive.official-documents.co.uk/document/doh/newnhs/contents.htm (accessed on 16 May 2011).

Department of Health (1989). *Working for Patients: The health services: caring for the 1990s*. Cm 555. London: Her Majesty's Stationery Office.

Department of Trade and Industry (2002). *Social Enterprise: A strategy for success*. London: Department of Trade and Industry. Available at: www.uk.coop/system/files/sites/default/files/se_strategy_2002.pdf (accessed on 10 May 2011).

Dickinson H, Peck E, Smith JA (2006). *Leadership in Organisational Transition: What can we learn from the research evidence?* Birmingham: Health Services Management Centre/NHS Institute of Innovation and Improvement.

Dismuke CE, Guimaraes P (2002). 'Has the caveat of case-mix based payment influenced the quality of inpatient hospital care in Portugal?'. *Applied Economics*, vol 34, no 10, pp 1301–7.

Dixon A, Ham C (2010). *Liberating the NHS: The right prescription in a cold climate?* London: The King's Fund. Available at: www.kingsfund.org.uk/document.rm?id=8780 (accessed on 14 May 2011).

Dixon A, Robertson R, Appleby J, Burge P, Devlin N, Magee H (2010a). *Patient Choice: How patients choose and how providers respond*. London: The King's Fund. Available at: www.kingsfund.org.uk/document.rm?id=8687 (accessed on 10 May 2011).

Dixon A, Robertson R, Bal R (2010b). 'The experience of implementing choice at point of referral: a comparison of the Netherlands and England.' *Health Economics, Policy and Law*, vol 5, no 3, pp 295–317.

Doctors.net (2005). *Knowledge of the Choose and Book Programme Amongst GPs in England: An update of the 2004 survey of GPs' opinions for the National Audit Office* [online]. Available at: www.nao.org.uk/idoc.ashx?docId=518EF7FE-D9AD-413B-A622-D5520658A6C6&version=-1 (accessed on 14 May 2011).

Dowling B (1997). 'Effect of fundholding on waiting times: database study'. *British Medical Journal*, vol 315, no 7103, pp 290–2.

Dowling B, Glendinning C (eds) (2003). *The New Primary Care: Modern, dependable, successful?* Maidenhead: Open University Press.

Dranove D, Lindrooth R (2003). 'Hospital consolidation and costs: another look at the evidence'. *Journal of Health Economics*, vol 22, no 6, pp 983–97.

Dranove D, Ludwick R (1999). 'Competition and pricing by nonprofit hospitals: a reassessment of Lynk's analysis'. *Journal of Health Economics*, vol 18, no 1, pp 87–98.

Dranove D, Satterthwaite MA (2000). 'The industrial organization of health care markets', in Culyer AJ, Newhouse JP (eds), *Handbook of Health Economics*, volume 1, part 2, chapter 20, pp 1093–139. Amsterdam: Elsevier.

Durand M, Hutchings A, Black N, Green J (2010). '"Not quite Jericho, but more doors than there used to be". Staff views of the impact of "modernization" on boundaries around adult critical care services in England'. *Journal of Health Services Research & Policy*, vol 15, no 4, pp 229–35.

Dusheiko M, Gravelle H, Jacobs R (2004). 'The effect of practice budgets on patient waiting times: allowing for selection bias'. *Health Economics*, vol 13, no 10, pp 941–58.

Edwards N (2005). 'Using markets to reform health care'. *British Medical Journal*, vol 331, no 7530, pp 1464–6.

Edwards N, Lewis R (2008). 'Who owns and operates healthcare providers and does it matter?'. *Journal of the Royal Society of Medicine*, vol 101, no 2, pp 54–8.

Eggleston K, Shen Y-C, Lau J, Schmid CH, Chan J (2006). *Hospital Ownership and Quality of Care: What explains the different results?* Working Paper no 12241. Cambridge, MA: National Bureau of Economic Research.

Ellins J, Ham C, Parker H (2008). *Choice and Competition in Primary Care: Much ado about nothing?* Policy Paper 2. Birmingham: Health Services Management Centre.

Enthoven AC (2000). 'In pursuit of an improving National Health Service'. *Health Affairs*, vol 19, no 3, pp 102–19.

Enthoven A (1985). *Reflections on the Management of the National Health Service: An American looks at incentives to efficiency in health service management in the UK*. London: Nuffield Provincial Hospitals Trust.

Escarce JJ, Van Horn RL, Pauly MV, Williams SV, Shea JA, Chen W (1999). 'Health maintenance organizations and hospital quality for coronary artery bypass surgery'. *Medical Care Research and Review*, vol 56, no 3, pp 340–62.

Exworthy M, Frosini F, Peckham S, Powell M, Greener I, Holloway JA (2009). *Decentralisation and Performance: Autonomy and incentives in local health economies.* Southampton: National Co-ordinating Centre for the NHS Service Delivery and Organisation (NCCSDO) R&D.

Farrar S, Yi D, Sutton M, Chalkley M, Sussex J, Scott A (2009). 'Has payment by results affected the way that English hospitals provide care? Difference-in-differences analysis'. *British Medical Journal,* no 339, p b3047.

Farrar S, Sussex J, Yi D, Sutton M, Chalkley M, Scott A, Ma A (2007). *National Evaluation of Payment by Results.* Report to the Department of Health. Aberdeen: Health Economics Research Unit. Available at: www.abdn.ac.uk/heru/documents/pbr_report_dec07.pdf (accessed on 10 May 2011).

Federal Trade Commission/US Department of Justice (2004). *Improving Health Care: A dose of competition.* Washington, DC: Federal Trade Commission/Department of Justice. Available at: www.justice.gov/atr/public/health_care/204694.pdf (accessed on 13 May 2011).

Ferlie E (1994). 'The creation and evolution of quasi-markets in the public sector: early evidence from the National Health Service'. *Policy and Politics,* vol 22, no 2, pp 105–12.

Ferlie E, Freeman G, McDonnell J, Petsoulas C, Rundle-Smith S (2005). *NHS London Patient Choice Project: Evaluation Organisational Process Strand Final Report.* London: Royal Holloway, University of London and Imperial College London.

Ferrier GD, Valdmanis VG (2004). 'Do mergers improve hospital productivity?' *Journal of the Operational Research Society,* vol 55, no 10, pp 1071–80.

Figueras J, Robinson R, Jakubowski E (2005). 'Purchasing to improve health systems performance: drawing the lessons', in Figueras J, Robinson R, Jakubowski E (eds), *Purchasing to Improve Health System Performance.* Maidenhead: Open University Press.

Fosberg E, Axelsson R, Arnetz B (2000). 'Effects of performance-based reimbursement in health care'. *Scandinavian Journal of Public Health,* vol 28, no 2, pp 102–10.

Fotaki M, Boyd A, McDonald R, Smith L, Roland M, Edwards A, Elwyn G, Sheaff R (2005). *Patient Choice and the Organisation and Delivery of Health Services: Scoping Review.* Report for the National Co-ordinating Centre for NHS Service Delivery and Organisation R&D. Manchester: Centre for Public Policy and Management, Manchester Business School, University of Manchester. Available at: www.escholar.manchester.ac.uk/api/datastream?publicationPid=uk-ac-man-scw:5b699&datastreamId=FULL-TEXT.PDF (accessed on 13 May 2011).

Francis R (2010). *The Mid Staffordshire NHS Foundation Trust Inquiry: Independent Inquiry into care provided by Mid Staffordshire NHS Foundation Trust, January 2005–March 2009.* HC 375-I Session 2009/10. London: The Stationery Office. Available at: www.dh.gov.uk/en/Publicationsandstatistics/Publications/PublicationsPolicyAndGuidance/DH_113018 (accessed on 14 May 2011).

Garratt E (2009). *The Key Findings Report for the 2008 Inpatient Survey: Acute Co-Ordination Centre for the NHS Patient Survey Programme.* Oxford: Picker Institute Europe, p 98. Available at: www.nhssurveys.org/Filestore/documents/Key_Findings_report_for_the_2008__Inpatient_Survey.pdf (accessed on 25 May 2011).

Gaskin DJ, Escarce JJ, Schulman K, Hadley J (2002). 'The determinants of HMOs' contracting with hospitals for bypass surgery'. *Health Services Research*, vol 37, no 4, pp 963–84.

Gaynor M (2004). *Competition and Quality in Health Care Markets: What do we know, what don't we know?* Paper commissioned by the Federal Trade Commission. Pittsburgh, PA: Department of Public Policy, Carnegie Mellon University.

Gaynor M, Haas-Wilson D (1999). 'Change, consolidation, and competition in health care markets'. *Journal of Economic Perspectives*, vol 13, no 1, pp 141–64.

Gaynor M, Vogt WB (2003). 'Competition among hospitals'. *Rand Journal of Economics*, vol 34, no 4, pp 764–85.

Gaynor MS, Vogt WB (2000). 'Antitrust and competition in health care markets', in Culyer AJ, Newhouse JP (eds), *Handbook of Health Economics.* Elsevier: Amsterdam.

Gaynor M, Moreno-Serra R, Propper C (2011). *Death by Market Power: Reform, competition and patient outcomes in the National Health Service, updated August 2011.* Working Paper no 10/242. Bristol: the Centre for Market and Public Organisation, Bristol Institute of Public Affairs, University of Bristol. Available at: www.bristol.ac.uk/cmpo/publications/papers/2010/wp242.pdf (accessed on 15 August 2011).

Giddens A (1998). *The Third Way: The renewal of social democracy.* Cambridge: Polity Press.

Gillam S, Lewis R (2009). 'Practice based commissioning in the UK: reinvigoration will require more than just extra funding'. *British Medical Journal*, vol 338, b832. Available at: www.bmj.com/content/338/bmj.b832.full?sid=056787c4-c3fe-4548-87a6-bdd4d18c370e (accessed on 14 May 2011).

Glennerster H, Matsaganis M, Owens P, Hancock S (1994). *Implementing GP Fundholding: Wildcard or winning hand.* London: Open University Press.

Goodwin N (1998). 'GP fundholding', in Le Grand J, Mays N, Mulligan JA (eds), *Learning from the NHS Internal Market: A review of the evidence*, pp 43–68. London: The King's Fund.

Goodwin N, Dixon A, Poole T, Raleigh V (2011). *Improving the Quality of Care in General Practice: Report of an independent inquiry commissioned by The King's Fund*. London: The King's Fund. Available at: www.kingsfund.org.uk/document. rm?id=9040 (accessed on 14 May 2011).

Gowrisankaran G, Town RJ (2003). 'Competition, payers, and hospital quality'. *Health Services Research*, vol 38, no 6 (part 1), pp 1403–21.

Greener I (2007). 'Are the assumptions underlying patients choice realistic? A review of the evidence'. *British Medical Bulletin*, vol 83, no 1, pp 249–58. Available at: http://bmb.oxfordjournals.org/content/83/1/249.full (accessed on 18 May 2011).

Greener I, Mannion R (2009a). 'A realistic evaluation of practice-based commissioning'. *Policy & Politics*, vol 37, no 1, pp 57–73.

Greener I, Mannion R (2009b). 'Patient choice in the NHS: what is the effect of choice policies on patients and relationships in health economies?'. *Public Money & Management*, vol 29, no 2, pp 95–100.

Greer SL (2004). *Territorial Politics and Health Policy: UK health policy in comparative perspective*. Manchester: Manchester University Press.

Grindle M, Thomas J (1991). *Public Choices and Policy Change: The political economy of reform in developing countries*. Baltimore, MD: Johns Hopkins University Press.

Groot T, Budding T (2008). 'New public management's current issues and future prospects'. *Financial Accountability & Management*, vol 24, no 1, pp 1–13.

Grout P, Stevens M (2003). 'The assessment: financing and managing public services'. *Oxford Review of Economic Policy*, vol 19, no 2, pp 215–34.

Haas-Wilson D (2003). *Managed Care and Monopoly Power: The antitrust challenge*. Cambridge, MA: Harvard University Press.

Ham C (2011). 'GPs will walk a tightrope between making or buying'. Health Service Journal website, online opinion piece, 6 January. Available at: www. hsj.co.uk/comment/opinion/gps-will-walk-a-tightrope-between-making-or-buying/5023312.article (accessed on 14 May 2011).

Ham C (2008). 'World class commissioning: a health policy chimera?'. *Journal of Health Services Research & Policy*, vol 13, no 2, pp 116–21.

Ham C (2007). *Competition and Collaboration in the English Health Reforms*. Seminar Note. London: The Nuffield Trust.

Ham C, Hunt P (2008). *Membership Governance in NHS Foundation Trusts: A review for the Department of Health*. Birmingham: Health Services Management Centre, University of Birmingham.

Ham C, Smith JA, Eastmure E (2011). *Commissioning Integrated Care in a Liberated NHS*. London: The Nuffield Trust.

Harrison A, Appleby J (2009). 'Reducing waiting times for hospital treatment: lessons from the English NHS'. *Journal of Health Services Research & Policy*, vol 14, no 3, pp 168–73.

Harrison TD (2007). 'Consolidations and closures: an empirical analysis of exits from the hospital industry'. *Health Economics*, 16, no 5, pp 457–74.

Hart O, Shleifer A, Vishnay R (1997). 'The proper scope of government: theory and application to prisons'. *Quarterly Journal of Economics*, vol 112, no 4, pp 1127–61.

Hauck K, Street A (2007). 'Do targets matter? A comparison of English and Welsh national health priorities'. *Health Economics*, vol 16, no 3, pp 275–90.

Healthcare Commission (2009a). *Investigation into Mid Staffordshire NHS Foundation Trust*. London: Healthcare Commission. Available at: www.cqc.org. uk/_db/_documents/Investigation_into_Mid_Staffordshire_NHS_Foundation_ Trust.pdf (accessed on 14 May 2011).

Healthcare Commission (2009b). *The Healthcare Commission 2004–2009: Regulating healthcare experience and lessons*. London: Healthcare Commission. Available at: www.cqc.org.uk/_db/_documents/Healthcare_Commission_legacy_ report.pdf (accessed on 14 May 2011).

Healthcare Commission (2008a). *Independent Sector Treatment Centres: The evidences so far*. London: Healthcare Commission. Available at: www.cqc.org.uk/_ db/_documents/Independent_sector_treatment_centres_The_evidense_so_far.pdf (accessed on 14 May 2011).

Healthcare Commission (2008b). *Learning from Investigations*. London: Healthcare Commission. Available at: www.cqc.org.uk/_db/_documents/ Learning_from_investigations.pdf (accessed on 14 May 2011).

Healthcare Commission (2008c). *Making a difference? An evaluation of the performance of the Healthcare Commission 2004–2008*. London: Healthcare Commission. Available at: www.chai.org.uk/_db/_documents/Making_a_ difference_evaluation_report_final.pdf (accessed on 14 May 2011).

Healthcare Commission (2008d). *The Annual Health Check 2007/08: A national overview of the performance of NHS trusts in England*. London: Commission for Healthcare Audit and Inspection. Available at: www.cqc.org.uk/_db/_ documents/0708_annual_health_check_overview_document.pdf (accessed on 14 May 2011).

Healthcare Commission (2007a). *Independent Sector Treatment Centres: A review of the quality of care*. London: Healthcare Commission. Available at: www.cqc.org. uk/_db/_documents/ISTC_Final_Tagged_200903243502.pdf (accessed on 14 May 2011).

Healthcare Commission (2007b). *The Annual Health Check 2006/2007. A national overview of the performance of NHS trusts in England*. London: Healthcare Commission. Available at: www.cqc.org.uk/_db/_documents/Annual_health_check_national_overview_2006-2007.pdf (accessed on 14 May 2011).

Healthcare Commission (2006a). *Investigation into Outbreaks of Clostridium difficile at Stoke Mandeville Hospital, Buckinghamshire Hospitals NHS Trust*. London: Health Care Commission. Available at: www.cqc.org.uk/_db/_documents/Stoke_Mandeville.pdf (accessed on 14 May 2011).

Healthcare Commission (2006b). *The Annual Health Check: Assessing and rating the NHS. NHS performance ratings 2005/2006*. London: Healthcare Commission. Available at: www.cqc.org.uk/_db/_documents/Performance_ratings_0506.pdf (accessed on 14 May 2011).

Healthcare Commission (2006c). *The Annual Health Check in 2006/2007: Assessing and rating the NHS*. London: Healthcare Commission. Available at: www.cqc.org.uk/_db/_documents/The_annual_health_check_in_2006_2007_assessing_and_rating_the_NHS_200609225143.pdf (accessed on 08 June 2011).

Healthcare Commission (2005a). '2005 Performance Ratings'. Healthcare Commission website. Available at: http://ratings2005.healthcarecommission.org.uk/ (accessed on 14 May 2011).

Healthcare Commission (2005b). *The Healthcare Commission's Review of NHS Foundation Trusts*. London: Healthcare Commission. Available at: www.cqc.org.uk/_db/_documents/4815-Foundation_Trusts-v10.pdf (accessed on 14 May 2011).

Healthcare Commission (2004). '2004 Performance Ratings'. Healthcare Commission website. Available at: http://ratings2004.healthcarecommission.org.uk/ (accessed on 14 May 2011).

Heclo H (1974). *Modern Social Politics in Britain and Sweden*. New Haven: Yale University Press.

Her Majesty's Government (2011). 'Health and Social Care Bill 2010–2011'. Parliament website. Available at: http://services.parliament.uk/bills/2010-11/healthandsocialcare.html (accessed on 21 May 2011).

Her Majesty's Government (2010). *The Coalition: Our programme for government*. London: The Cabinet Office. Available at: www.cabinetoffice.gov.uk/sites/default/files/resources/coalition_programme_for_government.pdf (accessed on 10 May 2011).

Ho V, Hamilton BH (2000). 'Hospital mergers and acquisitions: does market consolidation harm patients?' *Journal of Health Economics*, vol 19, no 5, pp 767–91.

Hodge G (2000). *Privatisation: An international review of performance*. Boulder, Co: Westview Press.

Hopkins A (2007). *Delivering Public Services: Service users' experiences of the third sector*. A report to the Office of the Third Sector. London: National Consumer Council.

House of Commons Health Committee (2011). *Commissioning: Further issues.* Fifth report of session 2010–11. Volume 1. HC 796-I. London: The Stationery Office. Available at: www.publications.parliament.uk/pa/cm201011/cmselect/cmhealth/796/79602.htm#evidence (accessed on 11 July 2011).

House of Commons Health Committee (2010a). *Commissioning: Fourth report of session 200910.* Volume 1. HC 268-I. London: The Stationery Office. Available at: www.publications.parliament.uk/pa/cm200910/cmselect/cmhealth/268/268i.pdf (accessed on 14 May 2011).

House of Commons Health Committee (2010b). *Public Expenditure on Health and Personal Social Services 2009: Memorandum received from the Department of Health containing replies to a written questionnaire from the committee.* HC 269-i. London: The Stationery Office. Available at: www.parliament.the-stationery-office.co.uk/pa/cm200910/cmselect/cmhealth/269/269i.pdf (accessed on 14 May 2011).

House of Commons Health Committee (2009). *Patient Safety: Sixth report of session 2008–09.* Volume I. HC 151-I. London: The Stationery Office. Available at: www.publications.parliament.uk/pa/cm200809/cmselect/cmhealth/151/151i.pdf (accessed on 14 May 2011).

House of Commons Health Committee (2008). *Foundation Trusts and Monitor.* Sixth report of session 2007–08. Volume 1. HC 833-I. London: The Stationery Office. Available at: www.parliament.the-stationery-office.co.uk/pa/cm200708/cmselect/cmhealth/833/833.pdf (accessed on 14 May 2011).

House of Commons Health Committee (2006). *Independent Sector Treatment Centres.* Fourth report of session 2005–06. Volume 1. HC 934-I. London: The Stationery Office. Available at: www.parliament.the-stationery-office.co.uk/pa/cm200506/cmselect/cmhealth/934/934i.pdf (accessed on 14 May 2011).

Iacobucci G (2009). 'Recession forces Chilvers McCrea to drop APMS contract'. *Pulse*, 28 April. Available at: www.pulsetoday.co.uk/story.asp?sectioncode=23&storycode=4122532 (accessed on 14 May 2011).

Imison C, Naylor C (2010). *Referral Management: Lessons for success.* London: The King's Fund. Available at: www.kingsfund.org.uk/document.rm?id=8736 (accessed on 14 May 2011).

Imison C, Naylor C, Maybin J (2008). *Under One Roof: Will polyclinics deliver integrated care?* London: The King's Fund .

Jacobs R, Smith P (2004). *A Descriptive Analysis of General Acute Trust Star Ratings.* Discussion Paper 189. York: Centre for Health Economics, University of York. Available at: www.york.ac.uk/media/che/documents/papers/discussionpapers/CHE%20Discussion%20Paper%20189.pdf (accessed on 14 May 2011).

Jacobs R, Martin S, Goddard M, Gravelle H, Smith P (2006). 'Exploring the determinants of NHS performance ratings: lessons for performance assessment systems'. *Journal of Health Services Research & Policy*, vol 11, no 4, pp 211–17.

Joskow PL (1980). 'The effects of competition and regulation on hospital bed supply and the reservation quality of the hospital'. *Bell Journal of Economics*, vol 11, no 2, pp 421–47.

Kahn KL, Rubenstein LV, Draper D, Kosecoff J, Rogers WH, Keeler EB, Brook RH. (1990). 'The effects of the DRG-based prospective payment system on the quality of care for hospitalized Medicare patients'. *Journal of the American Medical Association*, vol 264, no 15, pp 1953–5.

Kastberg G, Siverbo S (2007). 'Activity-based financing of health care – experiences from Sweden'. *International Journal of Health Planning and Management*, vol 22, no 1, pp 25–44.

Kay A (2002). 'The abolition of the GP fundholding scheme: a lesson in evidence-based policy making'. *British Journal of General Practice*, vol 52, no 475, pp 141–4.

Keeler EB, Melnick G, Zwanziger J (1999). 'The changing effects of competition on non-profit and for-profit hospital pricing behavior'. *Journal of Health Economics*, vol 18, no 1, pp 69–86.

Keen J, Light D, Mays N (2001). *Public–Private Relations in Health Care*. London: The King's Fund.

Kennedy I (2001). *The Report of the Public Inquiry into Children's Heart Surgery at the Bristol Royal Infirmary 1984–1995. Learning from Bristol*. CM 5207(l). London: The Stationery Office. Available at: www.bristol-inquiry.org.uk/final_report/the_report.pdf (accessed on 16 May 2011).

Kessler DP, Geppert JJ (2005). 'The effects of competition on variation in the quality and cost of medical care'. *Journal of Economics and Management Strategy*, vol 14, no 3, pp 575–89. Available at: www.ftc.gov/be/healthcare/wp/02_Kessler_Geppert_TheEffectsofCompetitiononVariation.pdf (accessed on 14 May 2011).

Kessler DP, McClellan MB (2000). 'Is hospital competition socially wasteful?' *Quarterly Journal of Economics*, vol 115, pp 577–615.

Kjerstad E (2003). 'Prospective funding of general hospitals in Norway – incentives for higher production?'. *International Journal of Health Care Finance and Economics*, vol 3, no 4, pp 231–51.

Klein R (2006). *The New Politics of the NHS: From creation to reinvention*, 5th edn. Abingdon: Radcliffe Publishing.

Kosecoff J, Kahn KL, Rogers WH, Reinisch EJ, Sherwood MJ, Rubenstein LV, Draper D, Roth CP, Chew C, Brook RH (1990). 'Prospective payment system and impairment at discharge: the "quicker-and-sicker" story revisited'. *Journal of the American Medical Association*, vol 264, no 15, pp 1980–3.

Le Grand J (2007). *The Other Invisible Hand: Delivering public services through choice and competition*. Princeton, NJ: Princeton University Press.

Le Grand J (1999). 'Competition, cooperation, or control? Tales from the British National Health Service'. *Health Affairs*, vol 18, no 3, pp 27–39.

Le Grand J, Mays N, Mulligan J (eds) (1998). *Learning from the NHS Internal Market: A review of the evidence*. London: The King's Fund.

Le Maistre N, Reeves R, Coulter A (2003). *Patients' Experience of CHD Choice*. Oxford: Picker Institute Europe.

Lewis R, Hinton L (2008). 'Citizen and staff involvement in health service decision-making: have National Health Service foundation trusts in England given stakeholders a louder voice?' *Journal of Health Services Research & Policy*, vol 13, no 1, pp 19–25.

Lewis R, Rosen R, Goodwin N, Dixon J (2010). *Where Next for Integrated Care Organisations in the English NHS?* London: The Nuffield Trust. Available at: www.nuffieldtrust.org.uk/members/download.aspx?f=%2fecomm%2ffiles%2fWhere_next_ICO_KF_NT_230310.pdf&a=skip (accessed on 14 May 2011).

Lewis R, Smith J, Harrison A (2009). 'From quasi-market to market in the National Health Service in England: what does this mean for the purchasing of health services?' *Journal of Health Services Research & Policy*, vol 14, no 1, pp 44–51.

Lewis R, Mays N, Curry N, Robertson R (2007). 'Implementing practice based commissioning'. Editorial. *British Medical Journal*, vol 335, no 7631, p 1168.

Light DW (1997). 'From managed competition to managed cooperation: theory and lessons from the British experience'. *The Millbank Quarterly*, vol 75, no 3, pp 297–341.

Lim JNW, Edlin R (2009). 'Preferences of older patients and choice of treatment location in the UK: a binary choice experiment'. *Health Policy*, vol 91, no 3, pp 252–7.

Lipsky M (1980). *Street-Level Bureaucracy: Dilemmas of the individual in public services*. New York: Russel Sage Foundation.

Local Government Association (2008). *Who's Accountable for Health? LGA health commission final report*. London: Local Government Association. Available at: www.lga.gov.uk/lga/aio/721828 (accessed on 14 May 2011).

Magee H, Davis LJ, Coulter A (2003). 'Public views on healthcare performance indicators and patient choice'. *Journal of the Royal Society of Medicine*, vol 96, no 7, pp 338–42.

Majeed F, Chaturvedi N, Reading R, Ben-Shlomo Y (1994). 'Equity in the NHS. Monitoring and promoting equity in primary and secondary care'. *British Medical Journal*, vol 308, no 6941, pp 1426–9.

Mannion R, Harrison S, Jacobs R, Konteh F, Walshe K, Davies HT (2009). 'From cultural cohesion to rules and competition: the trajectory of senior management culture in English NHS hospitals, 2001–2008'. *Journal of the Royal Society of Medicine*, vol 102, no 8, pp 332–6.

Mannion R, Goddard M, Bate A (2007). 'Aligning incentives and motivations in health care: the case of earned autonomy'. *Financial Accountability and Management*, vol 23, no 4, pp 401–20.

Mannion R, Marini G, Street A (2006). 'Demand management and administrative costs under payment by results'. *Health Policy Matters*, no 12, pp 1–8. Available at: www.york.ac.uk/media/healthsciences/documents/research/hpm12.pdf (accessed on 14 May 2011).

Mannion R, Davies H, Marshall M (2005). 'Impact of star performance ratings in English acute hospital trusts'. *Journal of Health Services Research & Policy*, vol 10, no 1, pp 18–24.

Marini G, Miraldo M, Jacobs R, Goddard M (2008). 'Giving greater financial independence to hospitals – does it make a difference? The case of English NHS Trusts'. *Health Economics*, vol 17, no 6, pp 751–75.

Marmot M (2010). *Fair Society, Healthy Lives: The Marmot review. Strategic review of health inequalities in England post-2010*. London: The Marmot Review. Available at: www.marmotreview.org/AssetLibrary/pdfs/Reports/FairSocietyHealthyLives. pdf (accessed on 14 May 2011).

Marshall M, McLoughlin V (2010). 'How do patients use information on providers?'. *British Medical Journal*, vol 341, no c5272.

Mason A, Wilkin D, Whitehouse C (1994). 'Choice of hospital for elective referrals: GPs' and patients' views', in Robinson R, Le Grand J (eds), *Evaluating the NHS Reforms*, pp 108–29. London: The King's Fund.

Matsaganis M, Glennerster H (1994). 'The threat of "cream skimming" in the post-reform NHS'. *Journal of Health Economics*, vol 13, no 1, pp 31–60.

Mays N, Hand K (2000). *A Review of Options for Health and Disability Support Purchasing in New Zealand*. Treasury working paper 00/20. Wellington: New Zealand Treasury. Available at: www.treasury.govt.nz/publications/research-policy/wp/2000/00-20/twp00-20.pdf (accessed on 14 May 2011).

Mays N, Wyke S, Malbon G, Goodwin G (eds) (2001). *The Purchasing of Health Care by Primary Care Organisations: An evaluation and guide to future policy*. Buckingham: Open University Press.

Mays N, Mulligan JA, Goodwin N (2000). 'The British quasi-market in health care: a balance sheet of the evidence'. *Journal of Health Services Research & Policy*, vol 5, no 1, pp 49–58.

Melnick GA, Zwanziger J, Bamezai A, Pattison R (1992). 'The effects of market structure and bargaining position on hospital prices'. *Journal of Health Economics*, vol 11, no 3, pp 217–33.

Mikkola H, Keskimäki I, Häkkinen U (2002). 'DRG-related prices applied in a public health care system – can Finland learn from Norway and Sweden?'. *Health Policy*, vol 59, no 1, pp 37–51.

Minott J, Helms D, Luft H, Guterman S, Weill H (2010). *The Group Employed Model as a Foundation for Health Care Delivery Reform*. Issue Brief. The Commonwealth Fund. April 9, publication 1389, volume 83. Available at: www.commonwealthfund.org/~/media/Files/Publications/Issue%20Brief/2010/Apr/1389_Minott_group_employed_model_hlt_reform_ib_v2.pdf (accessed on 14 May 2011).

Mohan J (2003). *Reconciling Equity and Choice? Foundation hospitals and the future of the NHS*. London: Catalyst.

Monitor (2011). 'What We Do'. Monitor website. Available at: www.monitor-nhsft.gov.uk/home/about-monitor/what-we-do (accessed on 8 June 2011).

Monitor (2010). 'NHS foundation trust directory'. Monitor website. Available at: www.monitor-nhsft.gov.uk/home/about-nhs-foundation-trusts/nhs-foundation-trust-directory (accessed on 8 October 2010).

Monitor/Frontier Economics (2010). *Measuring Monitor's Impact: Economic evaluation report*. London: Monitor. Available at: www.monitor-nhsft.gov.uk/sites/default/files/Measuring%20Monitors%20impact_published.pdf (accessed on 14 May 2011).

Mukamel DB, Zwanziger J, Tomaszewski KJ (2001). 'HMO penetration, competition, and risk-adjusted hospital mortality'. *Health Services Research*, vol 36, no 6 (part 1), pp 1019–35.

Mulligan JA (1998). 'Health authority purchasing', in LeGrand J, Mays N, Mulligan JA (eds), *Learning from the NHS Internal Market: A review of the evidence*, pp 20–42. London: The King's Fund.

National Audit Office (2010). *Memorandum by the National Audit Office (COM 119). Telephone survey of primary care trust commissioners*. Written evidence to the House of Commons health committee. Available at: www.parliament.the-stationery-office.co.uk/pa/cm200910/cmselect/cmhealth/268/268we15.htm (accessed on 14 May 2011).

National Audit Office (2007). *Improving Quality and Safety. Progress in implementing clinical governance in primary care: lessons for the new primary care trusts*. HC 100, session 2006–2007. London: The Stationery Office. Available at: www.nao.org.uk/idoc.ashx?docId=F3EE0F72-7E65-4C6D-BF4B-0B782BA1C566&version=-1 (accessed on 14 May 2011).

National Audit Office (2003). *Achieving Improvements Through Clinical Governance: A progress report on implementation by NHS trusts*. HC 1055, session 2002–2003. London: The Stationery Office. Available at: www.nao.org.uk/publications/0203/improvements_through_clinical.aspx (accessed on 14 May 2011).

Naylor N, Goodwin G (2010). *Building High-quality Commissioning: What role can external organisations play?* London: The King's Fund.

Newhouse J, Byrne D (1988). 'Did Medicare's prospective payment system cause length of stay to fall?'. *Journal of Health Economics*, vol 7, no 4, pp 413–16.

Newman J, Vidler E (2006). 'Discriminating customers, responsible patients, empowered users: consumerism and the modernisation of health care'. *Journal of Social Policy*, vol 35, no 2, pp 193–209.

NHS Alliance (2003). *What is the State of Commissioning in Primary Care Trusts?* Retford: NHS Alliance.

NHS Confederation (2010). *PCT World Class Commissioning Assurance Results 2009/10*. London: NHS Confederation. Available at: www.nhsconfed.org/Documents/PCT%20World%20Class%20Commissioning%20assurance%20results%202009.pdf (accessed on 15 May 2011).

NHS Confederation (2009). *Commissioning in a Cold Climate*. London: NHS Confederation PCT Network.

NHS Connecting for Health (2010). 'Choose and Book'. NHS Connecting for Health website. Available at: www.chooseandbook.nhs.uk/staff/overview/whouses (accessed on 10 May 2011).

NHS Future Forum (2011). *Summary Report on Proposed Changes to the NHS* [online]. Department of Health website. Available at www.dh.gov.uk/prod_consum_dh/groups/dh_digitalassets/documents/digitalasset/dh_127540.pdf (accessed on 1 July 2011).

NHS London (2007). *Healthcare for London: A framework for action*. Chair: Professor Sir Ara Darzi. London: NHS London. Available at: www.nhshistory.com/darzilondon.pdf (accessed on 11 July 2011).

Noether M (1988). 'Competition among hospitals'. *Journal of Health Economics*, vol 7, no 3, pp 259–84.

Office for Public Management (2008). *Evaluation of the Healthcare Commission's Assessment Process*. London: Office for Public Management.

Ovretveit J (1995). *Purchasing for Health: A multi-disciplinary introduction to the theory and practice of purchasing*. Buckingham: Open University Press.

Palmer K (2011). *Reconfiguring Hospital Services: Lessons from South East London*. London: The King's Fund. Available at: www.kingsfund.org.uk/document.rm?id=8972 (accessed on 14 May 2011).

Paton C (1995). 'Present dangers and future threats: some perverse incentives in the NHS reforms'. *British Medical Journal*, vol 310, no 6989, pp 1245–8.

Pawson R, Tilley N (1997). *Realistic Evaluation*. London: Sage.

Pears R (2009). 'What is the future for Spearhead PCTs?' *British Journal of Healthcare Management*, vol 15, no 1, pp 28–32.

Pérotin V, Zamora B, Reeves R, Bartlett W, Allen P (2011, forthcoming). 'Does hospital ownership affect patient experience? An investigation into public–private sector differences in England'.

Pollock AM, Godden S (2008). 'Independent sector treatment centres: evidence so far'. *British Medical Journal*, vol 336, no 7641, pp 421–4.

Pollock AM, Kirkwood G (2009). 'Independent sector treatment centres: learning from a Scottish case study'. *British Medical Journal*, vol 338, p b1421.

Pollock AM, Price D, Miller E, Viebrock E, Shaoul J, Mohan J (2007). *A literature review on the structure and performance of not-for-profit health care organisations*. Report for the National Co-ordinating Centre for NHS Service Delivery and Organisation R&D (NCCSDO). Southampton: NCCSDO. Available at: www.sdo.nihr.ac.uk/files/project/106-final-report.pdf (accessed on 14 May 2011).

Polverejan E, Gardiner JC, Bradley CJ, Holmes-Rovner M, Rovner D (2003). 'Estimating mean hospital cost as a function of length of stay and patient characteristics'. *Health Economics*, vol 12, no 11, 935–47.

Powell M, Millar R, Mulla A, Brown H, Fewtrell C, McLeod H, Goodwin N, Dixon A, Naylor C (2011). *Comparative Case Studies of Health Reform in England: Final report submitted to the Department of Health Policy Research Programme (PRP)*. Birmingham: Health Services Management Centre. Available at: www.hsmc.bham.ac.uk/news/pdfs/dh-final-report.pdf (accessed on 11 July 2011).

Preker A, Harding A, Travis P (2000). '"Make or buy" decisions in the production of healthcare goods and services: new insights from institutional economics and organizational theory'. *Bulletin of the World Health Organization*, vol 78, no 6, pp 779–90.

Propper C, Sutton M, Whitnall C, Windmeijer F (2010a). 'Incentives and targets in hospital care: evidence from a natural experiment'. *Journal of Public Economics*, vol 94, no 3–4, pp 318–35.

Propper C, Burgess S, Gossage D (2008a). 'Competition and quality: evidence from the NHS internal market 1991–9'. *The Economic Journal*, vol 118, no 525, pp 138–70.

Propper C, Sutton M, Whitnall C, Windmeijer F (2008b). 'Did "targets and terror" reduce waiting times in England for hospital care?'. *The Berkeley Electronic Journal of Economic Analysis and Policy*, vol 8, no 2, article 5. Available at: www.bepress.com/bejeap/vol8/iss2/art5 (accessed on 15 May 2011).

Propper C, Wilson D, Burgess S (2006). 'Extending choice in English health care: the implications of the economic evidence'. *Journal of Social Policy*, vol 35, no 4, pp 537–57.

Propper C, Burgess S, Green K (2004). 'Does competition between hospitals improve the quality of care? Hospital death rates and the NHS internal market'. *Journal of Public Economics*, vol 88, no 7–8, pp 1247–72.

Propper C, Croxson B, Shearer A (2002). 'Waiting times for hospital admissions: the impact of GP fundholding'. *Journal of Health Economics*, vol 21, no 2, pp 227–52.

Raftery J, Robinson R, Mulligan J, Forrest S (1996). 'Contracting in the NHS quasi-market'. *Health Economics*, vol 5, no 4, 353–62.

Raine R, Wong W, Scholes S, Ashton C, Obichere A, Ambler G (2010). 'Social variations in access to hospital care for patients with colorectal, breast, and lung cancer between 1999 and 2006: retrospective analysis of hospital episode statistics'. *British Medical Journal*, vol 340, p b5479.

Rainwater JA, Romano PS (2003). 'What data do california HMOs use to select hospitals for contracting?'. *American Journal of Managed Care*, vol 9, no 8, pp 553–61.

Right Care (2010). *The NHS Atlas of Variation in Healthcare: Reducing unwarranted variation to increase value and improve quality* [online]. Right Care website. Available at: www.rightcare.nhs.uk/atlas/qipp_nhsAtlas-LOW_261110c.pdf (accessed on 21 May 2011).

Roberts J (1993). 'Managing markets'. *Journal of Public Health Medicine*, vol 15, no 4, pp 305–10.

Robinson JC, Luft HS (1985). 'The impact of hospital market structure on patient volume, average length of stay, and the cost of care'. *Journal of Health Economics*, vol 4, no 4, pp 333–56.

Robinson R, Bevan G (2005). 'The interplay between economic and political logics: path dependency in health care in England'. *Journal of Health Politics, Policy and Law*, vol 30, no 1–2, pp 53–78.

Robinson R, Le Grand J (eds) (1994). *Evaluating the NHS Reforms*. London: The King's Fund.

Robinson S, Dickinson H, Williams I, Freeman T, Rumbold B, Spence K (2011). *Priority Setting: An exploratory study of English primary care trusts*. London: The Nuffield Trust.

Rogers R, Williams S, Jarman B, Aylin P (2005). '"HRG drift" and payment by results'. *British Medical Journal*, vol 330, no 7491, p 563.

Rogowski J, Jain AK, Escarce JJ (2007). 'Hospital competition, managed care, and mortality after hospitalization for medical conditions in California'. *Health Services Research*, vol 42, no 2, pp 682–705.

Roland M (2008). 'Assessing the options available to Lord Darzi'. *British Medical Journal*, vol 336, no 7645, pp 625–6.

Rosen R, Florin D, Hutt R (2007). *An Anatomy of GP Referral Decisions*. London: The King's Fund. Available at: www.kingsfund.org.uk/document.rm?id=6792 (accessed on 14 May 2011).

Rosenau PV, Lako CJ (2008). 'An experiment with regulated competition and individual mandates for universal health care: the new Dutch health insurance system'. *Journal of Health Politics, Policy and Law*, vol 33, no 6, pp 1031–55.

Rosenberg MA, Browne MJ (2001). 'The impact of the inpatient prospective payment system and diagnosis-related groups: a survey of the literature'. *North American Actuarial Journal*, vol 5, no 4, pp 84–94. Available at: www.soa.org/library/pdftest/journals/north-american-actuarial-journal/2001/october/new_naaj0110_6.pdf (accessed on 14 May 2011).

Sampson F, O'Cathain A, Strong M, Pickin M, Dixon S, Esmonde L (forthcoming). *Commissioning Processes in Primary Care Trusts: A repeated cross sectional survey of health care commissioners in England.*

Santry C (2011). 'In charge of the not-so-light anymore brigade', *Health Service Journal*, 28 July, pp 16–17.

Sari N (2002). 'Do competition and managed care improve quality?'. *Health Economics*, vol 11, no 7, pp 571–84.

Scally G, Donaldson LJ (1998). 'The NHS's 50 anniversary. Clinical governance and the drive for quality improvement in the new NHS in England'. *British Medical Journal*, vol 317, no 7150, pp 61–5.

Schulman KA, Rubenstein LE, Seils DM, Harris M, Hadley J, Escarce JJ (1997). 'Quality assessment in contracting for tertiary care services by HMOs: a case study of three markets'. *Joint Commission Journal on Quality Improvement*, vol 23, no 2, pp 117–27.

Schwappach DL, Strasmann TJ (2007). 'Does location matter? A study of the public's preferences for surgical care provision'. *Journal of Evaluation in Clinical Practice*, vol 13, no 2, pp 259–64.

Schwartz B (2004). *The Paradox of Choice: Why less is more*, chapter 15, pp 847, 890, 2000. New York: Harper Collins.

Scrivens E (2007) *The Healthcare Commission's Assessment Process for English Health Care*. Keele University: The Health Care Standards Unit.

Serdén L, Lindqvist R, Rosén M (2003). 'Have DRG-based prospective payment systems influenced the number of secondary diagnoses in health care administrative data?'. *Health Policy*, vol 65, no 2, pp 101–7.

Shaw CD (2004). 'Standards for better health: fit for purpose?' *British Medical Journal*, vol 329, pp 1250–1.

Shen YC (2003). 'The effect of financial pressure on the quality of care in hospitals'. *Journal of Health Economics*, vol 22, no 2, pp 243–69.

Shortell SM, Hughes EF (1988). 'The effects of regulation, competition, and ownership on mortality rates among hospital inpatients'. *New England Journal of Medicine*, vol 318, no 17, pp 1100–7.

Siciliani L, Hurst J (2005). 'Tackling excessive waiting times for elective surgery: comparative analysis of policies in 12 OECD countries'. *Health Policy*, vol 72, no 2, pp 201–15.

Silverman E, Skinner J (2004). 'Medicare upcoding and hospital ownership'. *Journal of Health Economics*, vol 23, no 2, pp 369–89.

Sloan F (1988). *Hospital Ownership and Costs and Quality of Care: Is there a dime's worth of difference?* National Bureau of Economic Research Working Paper, 6706.

Sloan F, Picone G, Taylor D, Chou S (2001). 'Hospital ownership and cost and quality of care: is there a dime's worth of difference?'. *Journal of Health Economics*, vol 20, no 1, pp 1–21.

Smith J, Charlesworth A (2011). *NHS Reforms in England: Managing the transition*. Policy Response. London: The Nuffield Trust. Available at: www.nuffieldtrust.org.uk/members/download.aspx?f=%2fecomm%2ffiles%2fNHS-reforms-in-England-managing-the-transition-Mar11.pdf&a=skip (accessed on 14 May 2011).

Smith JA, Goodwin N (2006). *Towards Managed Primary Care: The role and experience of primary care organisations*. Aldershot: Ashgate Publishing.

Smith JA, Curry N, Mays N, Dixon J (2010). *Where Next for Commissioning in the English NHS?* London: The Nuffield Trust/The King's Fund. Available at: www.nuffieldtrust.org.uk/members/download.aspx?f=%2fecomm%2ffiles%2fWhere_next_commissioning_KF_NT_230310.pdf&a=skip (accessed on 14 May 2011).

Smith JA, Wood J, Elias J (2009). *Beyond Practice-Based Commissioning: The local clinical partnership*. London: The Nuffield Trust/NHS Alliance. Available at: www.nuffieldtrust.org.uk/members/download.aspx?f=%2fecomm%2ffiles%2fBeyon d_PBC_09.11.24.pdf&a=skip (accessed on 14 May 2011).

Smith J, Dixon J, Mays N, McLeod H, Goodwin N, McClelland S, Lewis R, Wyke S (2005). 'Practice-based commissioning: applying the research evidence'. *British Medical Journal*, vol 331, pp 1397–9.

Smith J, Mays N, Dixon J, Goodwin N, Lewis R, McClelland S, McLeod H, Wyke S (2004). *A Review of the Effectiveness of Primary Care-Led Commissioning and its Place in the NHS*. London: The Health Foundation. Available at: www. health.org.uk/public/cms/75/76/313/518/A%20review%20of%20the%20 effectiveness%20%20of%20primary%20care%20led%20commissioning%20 and%20its%20place%20in%20the%20NHS%20reportpdf.pdf?realName=3firzu. pdf (accessed on 14 May 2011).

Smith JA, Walshe K, Hunter DJ (2001). 'The "redisorganisation" of the NHS: another reorganisation involving unhappy managers can only worsen the service'. *British Medical Journal*, vol 323, pp 1262–3. Available at: www.bmj.com/ content/323/7324/1262.full.pdf (accessed on 14 May 2011).

Smith P (1995). 'On the unintended consequences of publishing performance data in the public sector'. *International Journal of Public Administration*, vol 18, no 2–3, pp 277–310.

Smith R (1998). 'All changed, changed utterly. British medicine will be transformed by the Bristol case'. *British Medical Journal*, vol 316, no 7149, pp 1917–18.

Söderlund N, Csaba I, Gray A, Milne R, Raftery J (1997). 'Impact of the NHS reforms on English hospital productivity: an analysis of the first three years'. *British Medical Journal*, vol 315, no 7116, pp 1126–9.

Sood N, Buntin MB, Escarce JJ (2008). 'Does how much and how you pay matter? Evidence from the inpatient rehabilitation care prospective payment system'. *Journal of Health Economics*, vol 27, no 4, pp 1046–59.

Spiegelhalter DJ (2005). 'The mystery of the lost star: a statistical detective story'. *Significance*, vol 2, no 4, pp 150–3.

Stevens S (2004). 'Reform strategies for the English NHS'. *Health Affairs*, vol 23, no 3, pp 37–44.

Street A, Maynard A (2007). 'Activity based financing in England: the need for continual refinement of payment by results'. *Health Economics, Policy and Law*, vol 2 (part 4), pp 419–27.

Street A, Sawson AH (2004). 'Would Roman soldiers fight for the financial flows regime? The re-issue of Diocletian's English NHS'. *Public Money & Management*, vol 24, no 5, pp 301–8.

Sussex J (2009). *How fair? Competition between independent and NHS providers*. Briefing no 5. London: Office for Health Economics.

Thomson S, Dixon A (2006). 'Choices in health care: the European experience'. *Journal of Health Services Research and Policy*, vol 11, no 3, pp 167–71.

Thorlby R, Maybin J (eds) (2010). *A High-Performing NHS? A review of progress 1997–2010*. London: The King's Fund. Available at: www.kingsfund.org.uk/document.rm?id=8651 (accessed on 14 May 2011).

Thorlby R, Lewis R, Dixon J (2008). *Should Primary Care Trusts Be Made More Locally Accountable?* A King's Fund discussion paper. London: The King's Fund. Available at: www.kingsfund.org.uk/document.rm?id=7561 (accessed on 14 May 2011).

Tribal Newchurch (2009). *Social Enterprise Pathfinder Programme Evaluation: Final report*. London: Department of Health.

Tuohy C (1999). 'Dynamics of a changing health sphere: the United States, Britain and Canada'. *Health Affairs*, vol 18, no 3, pp 114–34.

Turner S, Allen P, Bartlett W, Perotin V (2011). 'Innovation and the English National Health Service: A qualitative study of the independent sector treatment centre programme'. *Social Science and Medicine*, vol 73, no 4, 522–9.

Van de Ven WP, Schut FT (2009). 'Managed competition in the Netherlands: still work-in-progress'. *Health Economics*, vol 18, no 3, pp 253–5.

Van Eyk HC, Baum FE, Blandford J (2001). 'Evaluating healthcare reform: the challenge of evaluating changing policy environments'. *Evaluation*, vol 7, no 4, pp 487–503.

Vincent-Jones P (2006). *The New Public Contracting: Regulation, responsiveness, relationality*. Oxford: Oxford University Press.

Vining A, Globerman S (1999). 'Contracting-out health care services: a conceptual framework'. *Health Policy*, vol 46, no 2, pp 77–96.

Volpp KGM, Williams SV, Waldfogel J, Silber JH, Schwartz JS, Pauly MV (2003). 'Market reform in New Jersey and the effect on mortality from acute myocardial infarction'. *Health Services Research*, vol 38, no 2, pp 515–33.

Wade E, Smith J, Peck E, Freeman T (2006). *Commissioning in the Reformed NHS: Policy into practice*. Birmingham: Health Services Management Centre/NHS Alliance, University of Birmingham. Available at: www.hsmc.bham.ac.uk/documents/alliance_report_23March06.pdf (accessed on 14 May 2011).

Walshe K (2010). 'Reorganisation of the NHS in England'. Editorial. *British Medical Journal*, vol 341, c3843.

Walshe K (2003). *Regulating Healthcare: A prescription for improvement?* Maidenhead: Open University Press.

Walshe K (1999). 'Improvement through inspection? The development of the new Commission for Health Improvement in England and Wales'. *Quality in Health Care*, vol 8, no 3, pp 191–201.

Walshe K, Smith J, Dixon J, Edwards N, Hunter DJ, Mays N, Normand C, Robinson R (2004). 'Primary care trusts: the dangers of premature reorganisation' [Editorial]. *British Medical Journal*, vol 329, pp 871–2.

Webster C (2002). *The National Health Service – A political history*. 2nd revised edn. Oxford: Oxford University Press.

Weisbrod BA (ed) (1988). *To Profit or Not to Profit: The commercial transformation of the nonprofit sector*. Cambridge: Cambridge University Press.

West D (2010). 'Government tells CQC to drop annual health check reviews'. *Health Service Journal*, 8 July. Available at: www.hsj.co.uk/topics/nhs-regulation-and-inspection/government-tells-cqc-to-drop-annual-health-check-reviews/5016885.article (accessed on 14 May 2011).

West RM, Cattle BA, Bouyssie M, Squire I, de Belder M, Fox KA, Boyle R, McLenachan JM, Batin PD, Greenwood DC, Gale CP (2011). 'Impact of hospital proportion and volume on primary percutaneous coronary intervention performance in England and Wales'. *European Heart Journal*, vol 32, no 6, pp 706–11.

Williamson OE (1985). *The Economic Institutions of Capitalism: Firms, markets, relational contracting*. New York: Free Press.

Wood J, Curry N (2009). *PBC Two Years On: Moving forward and making a difference*. London: The King's Fund. Available at: www.kingsfund.org.uk/document.rm?id=8394 (accessed on 14 May 2011).

Woodin J (2006). 'Healthcare commissioning and contracting', in Walshe K, Smith JA (eds), *Healthcare Management*, chapter 12, pp 201–23. Maidenhead: Open University Press.

Wyke S, Mays N, Street A, Bevan G, McLeod H, Goodwin N (2003). 'Should general practitioners purchase health care for their patients? The total purchasing experiment in Britain'. *Health Policy*, vol 65, no 3, pp 243–59.

Yi D, Pugh E, Farrar S (2007). 'The effect of payment by results on the HRG creep in English hospitals: an empirical investigation'. Oral presentation at the International Health Economics Association's 6th World Congress: Explorations in Health, Copenhagen, 8–11 July.

Young GJ, Burgess JE Jr, Valley D (2002). 'Competition among hospitals for HMO business: effect of price and nonprice attributes'. *Health Services Research*, vol 37, no 5, pp 1267–89.